JUNIOR GREAT BOOKS

SERIES 5

FIRST SEMESTER

◆ ◆ ◆

AN INTERPRETIVE READING, WRITING,

AND DISCUSSION CURRICULUM

JUNIOR GREAT BOOKS

SERIES 5   FIRST SEMESTER

THE GREAT BOOKS FOUNDATION

A nonprofit educational corporation

First Printing

9   8

Printed in the United States of America

Published and distributed by

THE GREAT BOOKS FOUNDATION
A nonprofit educational corporation

35 East Wacker Drive, Suite 2300

Chicago, IL 60601-2298

CONTENTS

PREFACE

SHARED INQUIRY

In Junior Great Books you will explore a number of outstanding stories. You will do this in a variety of ways: by taking notes as you read, by looking at important words and passages, and by sharing your questions and ideas about each story with your group. In each of these activities, you and your classmates will be working together with your teacher or leader, asking and answering questions about what the story means. You will be sharing what you discover with your classmates. This way of reading, writing, and discussion in Junior Great Books is called *shared inquiry.*

One of the good things about shared inquiry is that you can speak without worrying about whether what you say is "the right answer." Different ideas and points of view can all lead to a better understanding of the story. When you speak, the leader may ask you to back up what you have said, or urge you to develop your idea further. Others in your class may also respond to what you say. They, too, may be asked to support their statements or explain them more clearly. After listening to what others say, you may change your mind about your answer. Shared inquiry gives you the chance to learn both from the author and from one another.

Sometimes you will focus on a small part of the story; at other times, you will think about the story as a whole.

Whether you are working on your own or with others, in shared inquiry you will develop *interpretations* of what you read—you will be working to discover what the author wants to tell you or make you feel through his or her words.

WHAT IS INTERPRETATION?

Good writers do their work with care. There are reasons for everything they put into their stories. They try to include only what has a point and what fits—things needed to make a story clear, to make it interesting, and to keep it moving along. They waste few words. In really good stories, everything fits. Everything has an explanation. The parts are connected and support one another just as the posts and beams in a building do.

The parts of the story, because they are connected, help to explain one another. Authors do not point out exactly how the parts are connected, nor do they say in so many words why everything in a story happens as it does. For one thing, that would make the story dull. For another, they want stories to be convincing—to seem like real life. In real life, few things that happen come complete with explanations. We have to puzzle out the explanations for ourselves.

Stories, too, ask us to work out many explanations for ourselves. And the answers to our questions are in the story, waiting to be found. Every good author puts into a story all that a reader must know to understand what is happening and why. As we figure out for ourselves why the things an author puts in a story are there, we are interpreting what we read. To interpret a story is to explain its meaning—what happens in it, and why, and what the story is about.

ACTIVE READING

You will need to think hard about the stories you read in Junior Great Books—not just about *what* happens but also about *why* it happens the way it does. You will be reading each story at least twice. When you read a story for the first time, your mind is mainly on the action—on what the characters think, do, and say. As you read, the main question you ask is likely to be "What's going to happen next?" When you read a story for the second time, your mind will be free to raise new and different questions about it, and this will lead you to think of new questions to explore with your group. You will almost always notice details that you missed on your first reading, ones that can make you change your mind about why the characters behave as they do or how you feel about them. A second reading gives you the chance to think about the story as a whole without wondering what will happen next.

In shared inquiry, you will need to read with a pencil in hand and to make notes as you read. While you are reading, mark the words and passages in the story that strike you as really important, interesting, or surprising. Mark places that make you think of a question. Mark parts that give you ideas about what the story means. Your teacher or leader may also ask you to watch for particular things during your reading and to give them special attention. Your notes will remind you of your thoughts while reading and help you to find evidence to back up what you say.

QUESTIONS OF FACT, INTERPRETATION, AND EVALUATION

There are three kinds of questions that can be asked about a story in Junior Great Books: questions of fact, questions of interpretation, and questions of evaluation.

Questions of fact ask you to recall particular details or events from a story. Everything the author puts into the story is a fact in that story, even if some of the things couldn't happen in real life. In "Charles," the first story in this book, many of the facts are very close to what we see in our daily lives, but in other stories they won't be. A question of fact has only one correct answer.

Knowing and remembering the facts in a story is important. They are the basis for your opinions about the story's meaning. And you will use them to support your opinions.

Many times a leader will ask a factual question in order to get you to back up what you have said with evidence from the story. Suppose someone says, "Laurie acts fresh just the way Charles does sometimes." A leader might then ask, *How does Laurie act fresh?* This question can be answered by pointing to the place that reads "he spoke insolently to his father" and to other places in the story.

Now and then you will be asked a factual question that cannot be answered by looking at any one passage. For example, the question *Are Laurie's parents interested in hearing about Charles?* can only be answered "Yes." Although the story does not come right out and say so, their conversations with Laurie show that they are interested. Nothing in the story shows that they are not.

Questions of interpretation hold the central place in Junior Great Books. These are the questions that ask you to think carefully about what happens in a story and to consider what the story means. Unlike factual questions, they have more than a single good answer. Any answer that can be supported by factual evidence from the story will be a good one.

Some interpretive questions focus on a single passage or ask about a single event. Take, for example, this one: *Why does Laurie say "I didn't learn nothing" when his father asks him about his first day at school?* One answer is that Laurie really doesn't think he learned anything. Another, that he had a bad day and doesn't want to talk about it. Another, that he is just being fresh. Still another is that Laurie wants to show off to his father the new "tough" way of talking he has learned.

Other, more basic interpretive questions are asked about the meaning of the story as a whole. The answers will often be drawn from several places in the story. Here is one basic interpretive question for "Charles": *Why are Laurie's parents more interested in Charles's behavior in kindergarten than they are in their son's?* To answer this question, you need to think about how Laurie's parents react to Charles's behavior and to their son's behavior throughout the whole story.

Questions of evaluation ask how the story fits with your own experience and, after you have interpreted it, whether or not you agree with what the story is saying. As you read "Charles," you might wonder, *Should Laurie's parents punish him for being fresh?* or *Is Laurie too young to know any better?* In answering questions like these, you will be thinking more about yourself and your beliefs than about the story itself.

After reading the story, thinking about evaluative questions can be a good way of deciding how you feel about the author's ideas.

Since understanding literature is the main purpose of Junior Great Books, you will spend most of your time considering questions of interpretation. Questions of fact will help you support your opinions about what a story means. Questions of evaluation will help you put yourself in the place of the characters in the story. You will have many chances to answer evaluative questions in your writing after Shared Inquiry Discussion.

SHARED INQUIRY DISCUSSION

After you have read a story twice, taken notes, and shared some of your questions with your classmates, you will be ready to participate in Shared Inquiry Discussion. Shared Inquiry Discussion begins when the discussion leader asks an interpretive question, a question that can have more than one good answer. The leader is not sure which answer is the best, and hopes to discover several good answers during the discussion. Because there can be more than one good answer, it takes many minds to discover and explore those answers fully. By asking questions, the leader seeks to help everyone in the group think for themselves about what the story means.

THE RULES OF SHARED INQUIRY DISCUSSION

1. **Only people who have read the story may take part in Shared Inquiry Discussion.** If you haven't read the story, you can't help others understand its meaning. Ideas that do not come from firsthand knowledge of the story will confuse the other members of the group.

2. **Discuss only the story everyone has read.** If you try to use other stories or personal experiences to explain your ideas, those who aren't familiar with them won't be able to join in the discussion.

3. **Do not use other people's opinions about the story unless you can back them up with evidence of your own.** When you take another person's word for what the story means, you have stopped thinking for yourself. This rule does not mean you may never use an idea you get from someone else. But make sure you understand the idea and can support it with factual details from the story.

4. **Leaders may only ask questions; they may not answer them.** Leaders never offer their own opinions. Instead, they share their questions about the story's meaning. This rule encourages you to do your own thinking about the story, and to remember that the leader really wants your help in understanding it.

In Shared Inquiry Discussion you may speak directly to anyone in the group, and not just to the leader. You may ask questions of anyone but the leader, and you will be answering questions that others ask you. Since you are all working together to search for a story's meaning, try to listen carefully when others are speaking. If you don't understand what they are saying, ask them to repeat their comments or explain them more clearly. If you disagree with what they are saying, you can tell them so, always giving your reasons. Sometimes, too, you will be able to support what another member of the group has said by giving a reason no one else has thought of.

By the end of a good discussion everyone in your group will understand the story better than they did before you began to exchange ideas, build on one another's insights, and work out new interpretations. At the close of a discussion, everyone will seldom agree in every detail on what the story means, but that's part of what makes it interesting and fun to discuss the stories in Junior Great Books.

WRITING YOUR OWN INTERPRETIVE QUESTIONS

Writing interpretive questions is one of the best ways to think on your own about the meaning of a story. After you have read a story twice and taken notes, you will be ready to begin turning your ideas into interpretive questions. Some of the good ways to find interpretive questions are listed here, together with questions that were written for "Charles."

Look for words or passages that you think are important and that you wonder about. The words that are used to describe how Laurie talks about Charles, for instance, are sometimes surprising. Laurie "grins enormously" when he reports that Charles hit the teacher. But he "reports grimly" that Charles was so good the teacher gave him an apple. One reader turned these observations into this interpretive question:

Why does Laurie grin when he reports that Charles was bad in school, but speak "grimly" when he reports that Charles was good?

Look for parts of the story that you feel strongly about. As you read a story, ask questions about whatever makes you react with strong feelings. Look for places where you agree or disagree with the characters or with the author. For instance, one reader thought Laurie's father was being unfair when he said, "When you've got a Charles to deal with, this may mean he's only plotting." She asked:

Why is Laurie's father sure that Charles won't reform for long?

When you are curious about why a character in the story acts the way he or she does, ask a question about that. One reader, for example, was curious about the change that occurs in Laurie when he starts school. He wrote this interpretive question:

> *Why does Laurie start to act fresh at home after his first day at school?*

Let questions come out of your ideas about the meaning of the story. As you read, keep asking yourself what the author wants you to think about and experience through his or her words. Ask questions about that. One reader wondered why Laurie's parents always disapprove of Charles's behavior but seem to accept Laurie's. She asked:

> *Why are Laurie's parents so critical of the way Charles acts when they can't even control their own son?*

Interpretation begins with questions, the questions that come to you as you read. In working out the answers, you will arrive at a clearer idea of how the parts of the story fit together and have a better idea of its meaning.

CHARLES

Shirley Jackson

The day my son Laurie started kindergarten he renounced corduroy overalls with bibs and began wearing blue jeans with a belt; I watched him go off the first morning with the older girl next door, seeing clearly that an era of my life was ended, my sweet-voiced nursery-school tot replaced by a long-trousered, swaggering character who forgot to stop at the corner and wave goodbye to me.

He came home the same way, the front door slamming open, his cap on the floor, and the voice suddenly become raucous shouting, "Isn't anybody *here*?"

At lunch he spoke insolently to his father, spilled his baby sister's milk, and remarked that his teacher said we were not to take the name of the Lord in vain.

"How *was* school today?" I asked, elaborately casual.

"All right," he said.

"Did you learn anything?" his father asked.

Laurie regarded his father coldly. "I didn't learn nothing," he said.

"Anything," I said. "Didn't learn anything."

"The teacher spanked a boy, though," Laurie said, addressing his bread and butter. "For being fresh," he added, with his mouth full.

"What did he do?" I asked. "Who was it?"

Laurie thought. "It was Charles," he said. "He was fresh. The teacher spanked him and made him stand in a corner. He was awfully fresh."

"What did he do?" I asked again, but Laurie slid off his chair, took a cookie, and left, while his father was still saying, "See here, young man."

The next day Laurie remarked at lunch, as soon as he sat down, "Well, Charles was bad again today." He grinned enormously and said, "Today Charles hit the teacher."

"Good heavens," I said, mindful of the Lord's name, "I suppose he got spanked again?"

"He sure did," Laurie said. "Look up," he said to his father.

"What?" his father said, looking up.

"Look down," Laurie said. "Look at my thumb. Gee, you're dumb." He began to laugh insanely.

"Why did Charles hit the teacher?" I asked quickly.

"Because she tried to make him color with red crayons," Laurie said. "Charles wanted to color with green crayons so he hit the teacher and she spanked him and said nobody play with Charles but everybody did."

The third day—it was Wednesday of the first week—Charles bounced a see-saw onto the head of a little girl and made her bleed, and the teacher made him stay inside all during recess. Thursday Charles had to stand in a corner during story-time because he kept pounding his feet on the floor. Friday Charles was deprived of blackboard privileges because he threw chalk.

On Saturday I remarked to my husband, "Do you think kindergarten is too unsettling for Laurie? All this toughness, and bad grammar, and this Charles boy sounds like such a bad influence."

"It'll be all right," my husband said reassuringly. "Bound to be people like Charles in the world. Might as well meet them now as later."

On Monday Laurie came home late, full of news. "Charles," he shouted as he came up the hill; I was waiting anxiously on the front steps. "Charles," Laurie yelled all the way up the hill, "Charles was bad again."

"Come right in," I said, as soon as he came close enough. "Lunch is waiting."

"You know what Charles did?" he demanded, following me through the door. "Charles yelled so in school they sent a boy in from first grade to tell the teacher she had to make Charles keep quiet, and so

Charles had to stay after school. And so all the children stayed to watch him."

"What did he do?" I asked.

"He just sat there," Laurie said, climbing into his chair at the table. "Hi, Pop, y'old dust mop."

"Charles had to stay after school today," I told my husband. "Everyone stayed with him."

"What does this Charles look like?" my husband asked Laurie. "What's his other name?"

"He's bigger than me," Laurie said. "And he doesn't have any rubbers and he doesn't ever wear a jacket."

Monday night was the first Parent-Teachers meeting, and only the fact that the baby had a cold kept me from going; I wanted passionately to meet Charles's mother. On Tuesday Laurie remarked suddenly, "Our teacher had a friend come to see her in school today."

"Charles's mother?" my husband and I asked simultaneously.

"Naaah," Laurie said scornfully. "It was a man who came and made us do exercises, we had to touch our toes. Look." He climbed down from his chair and squatted down and touched his toes. "Like this," he said. He got solemnly back into his chair and said, picking up his fork, "Charles didn't even *do* exercises."

"That's fine," I said heartily. "Didn't Charles want to do exercises?"

"Naaah," Laurie said. "Charles was so fresh to the teacher's friend he wasn't *let* do exercises."

"Fresh again?" I said.

"He kicked the teacher's friend," Laurie said. "The teacher's friend told Charles to touch his toes like I just did and Charles kicked him."

"What are they going to do about Charles, do you suppose?" Laurie's father asked him.

Laurie shrugged elaborately. "Throw him out of school, I guess," he said.

Wednesday and Thursday were routine; Charles yelled during story hour and hit a boy in the stomach and made him cry. On Friday Charles stayed after school again and so did all the other children.

With the third week of kindergarten Charles was an institution in our family; the baby was being a Charles when she cried all afternoon; Laurie did a Charles when he filled his wagon full of mud and pulled it through the kitchen; even my husband, when he caught his elbow in the telephone cord and pulled telephone, ashtray, and a bowl of flowers off the table, said, after the first minute, "Looks like Charles."

During the third and fourth weeks it looked like a reformation in Charles; Laurie reported grimly at lunch on Thursday of the third week, "Charles was so good today the teacher gave him an apple."

"What?" I said, and my husband added warily, "You mean Charles?"

"Charles," Laurie said. "He gave the crayons around and he picked up the books afterward and the teacher said he was her helper."

"What happened?" I asked incredulously.

"He was her helper, that's all," Laurie said, and shrugged.

"Can this be true, about Charles?" I asked my husband that night. "Can something like this happen?"

"Wait and see," my husband said cynically. "When you've got a Charles to deal with, this may mean he's only plotting."

He seemed to be wrong. For over a week Charles was the teacher's helper; each day he handed things out and he picked things up; no one had to stay after school.

"The P.T.A. meeting's next week again," I told my husband one evening. "I'm going to find Charles's mother there."

"Ask her what happened to Charles," my husband said. "I'd like to know."

"I'd like to know myself," I said.

On Friday of that week things were back to normal. "You know what Charles did today?" Laurie demanded at the lunch table, in a voice slightly awed. "He told a little girl to say a word and she said it and the teacher washed her mouth out with soap and Charles laughed."

"What word?" his father asked unwisely, and Laurie said, "I'll have to whisper it to you, it's so bad." He got down off his chair and went around to his father. His father bent his head down and Laurie whispered joyfully. His father's eyes widened.

"Did Charles tell the little girl to say *that*?" he asked respectfully.

"She said it *twice*," Laurie said. "Charles told her to say it *twice*."

"What happened to Charles?" my husband asked.

"Nothing," Laurie said. "He was passing out the crayons."

Monday morning Charles abandoned the little girl and said the evil word himself three or four times, getting his mouth washed out with soap each time. He also threw chalk.

My husband came to the door with me that evening as I set out for the P.T.A. meeting. "Invite her over for a cup of tea after the meeting," he said. "I want to get a look at her."

"If only she's there," I said prayerfully.

"She'll be there," my husband said. "I don't see how they could hold a P.T.A. meeting without Charles's mother."

At the meeting I sat restlessly, scanning each comfortable matronly face, trying to determine which one hid the secret of Charles. None of them looked to me haggard enough. No one stood up in the meeting and apologized for the way her son had been acting. No one mentioned Charles.

After the meeting I identified and sought out Laurie's kindergarten teacher. She had a plate with a cup of tea and a piece of chocolate cake; I had a plate with a cup of tea and a piece of marshmallow cake. We maneuvered up to one another cautiously and smiled.

7

"I've been so anxious to meet you," I said. "I'm Laurie's mother."

"We're all so interested in Laurie," she said.

"Well, he certainly likes kindergarten," I said. "He talks about it all the time."

"We had a little trouble adjusting, the first week or so," she said primly, "but now he's a fine little helper. With occasional lapses, of course."

"Laurie usually adjusts very quickly," I said. "I suppose this time it's Charles's influence."

"Charles?"

"Yes," I said, laughing, "you must have your hands full in that kindergarten, with Charles."

"Charles?" she said. "We don't have any Charles in the kindergarten."

GHOST CAT

Donna Hill

It was growing so dark that Filmore had to stop reading; but as soon as he put his book down, he began to notice the loneliness again.

His mother had been driving without a word ever since they had turned onto this remote and bumpy road. Jodi was asleep, curled up in back with her stuffed animal friend. There was nothing to see out the window except black trees and shrubs along the roadside thrashing in the wind. To the west, through the trees, he could see that the sun had melted onto the horizon, but to the east the sky looked dark and bruised.

Suddenly his mother said, "That must be the house." She stopped the car.

Jodi sat up. "Are we here?" Jodi always awoke at once, alert and happy. She did not seem to know what loneliness and sorrow were. Jodi had glossy black curls and eyes like agates. She was little for her six years, but sturdy and fearless, as even Filmore would admit, but only to himself. To others, sometimes as a compliment, he said she was daft.

"You two wait here while I take a look," said their mother.

Filmore watched their mother walk along the path between the swaying, overgrown bushes. She looked small, walking alone, not much taller than his sister, in fact. Filmore whispered, "Jodi, don't you wish Daddy were here with us?"

Jodi was brushing down the apron of her animal friend.

"Remember last summer with Daddy?" Filmore said. "The beach, how broad and clean and dazzling it was? Remember what fun we had in the boat?"

Jodi turned her animal friend about, inspecting her from all sides.

"Here comes mother," Filmore said. "Let's not remind her of Daddy." But he needn't have warned Jodi. She seemed not to have heard a word.

"This is it," their mother said. "Help me with the bags, please, Filmore."

He and Jodi scrambled out of the car.

"Wait, wait!" Jodi called. "I dropped Mrs. Tiggy-winkle! Don't worry, Mrs. Tiggy-winkle! We'll never leave you! We love you!"

"What does she care," Filmore protested. For some reason he was annoyed with his sister. "She's only a stuffed hedgehog."

"She is not! She's a raccoon!"

"Listen, either she's a hedgehog or she's not Mrs. Tiggy-winkle!"

"Filmore, please," their mother said, pushing through the creaking gate.

A stone path led to a cottage perched on a little bluff overlooking the cove. Trees were sighing and moaning over the roof, and shrubs whispered at the door. The wind dropped suddenly as though the house were holding its breath, and Filmore could hear the push of waves up the beach and their scraping retreat over pebbles and shells.

His mother paused at the stoop to search through her bag for the key. Now Filmore could see scaling paint, shutters hanging loose, and windows opaque with dust. "What a dump!" he muttered.

When he saw his mother's face, he was sorry. His mother had gone back to teaching and labored to keep up their home; no one knew better than Filmore how hard it had been.

"The agent told us we'd have to take it as is," she said. "That's how we can afford it." She found the key, but could hardly shove the door open for sand that had sucked up against it.

"We came for the beach, anyway," Filmore said. "Who cares about the house! I wouldn't care if it was haunted!"

"Oh, I love the haunted house!" Jodi cried, bursting into the front room. "Oh, we have a big window with the whole black sky in it! Oh, and a fireplace! And rocking chairs!" The floor squealed under her feet as she ran around excitedly. "And here's the kitchen, with a black monster stove!"

Their mother laughed. She had the same dark curly hair, the same eyes as Jodi, and when she laughed, she did not look much older. "It's charming, really. Just needs a little work. But first we need some sleep."

They climbed narrow stairs and opened creaking doors to three small rooms with beds under dust covers. The covers pleased their mother and made Jodi laugh. "Ghosts and more ghosts!" she cried.

In his unfamiliar little room above the kitchen, Filmore kept waking in the night to whistles, squeals, and thumps that could have been ghosts in the house, that could have been anything sinister at all.

The next morning, Filmore woke to the melancholy crying of gulls. When he heard Jodi's light voice below, he pulled his clothes on hurriedly and went down to the kitchen.

"Good morning, dear," his mother said from the stove, where she was already cooking breakfast. "Did you sleep well?"

"I didn't sleep at all," Jodi put in cheerfully. "Neither did Mrs. Tiggy-winkle. We stayed awake all night and listened to the haunted house."

Filmore did not want to admit his own feelings. "You're daft!"

"Something is here, you know," Jodi insisted. "Something besides us!"

"And I know what it is." Their mother laughed. "Sand! We'll get rid of it right now."

The house was so small that sweeping and dusting upstairs and down did not take long, and still there was time for the beach before lunch.

To Filmore, the beach was even more disappointing than the house. It was narrow and deserted, with low, dispirited waves the color of mud as far as the eye could see. There were no houses in sight, just cliffs and scraggy pine trees at each end of the cove. Edging the sand were patches of weeds and damp brown rags of algae that smelled like vinegar. The stain that marked high tide was littered with broken shells, sticks like bones, and here and there a dead fish. A troupe of sandpipers ran up the beach and back, as though frantic to escape.

Jodi loved everything. She made up a joyful beach song as she built a sand dragon and then she pressed Filmore to go with her while she filled her bucket with shells and treasures.

Stumping along at her heels, Filmore demanded, "Why don't you ever talk about Daddy? You were his dear rabbit, don't forget!"

"Look, Filmore!" Jodi cried. "I found a sand dollar!"

After lunch, they drove out for supplies. "It will be fun to see the village and the shops," their mother said.

The village turned out to be only a few houses scattered along the road, and on the beach, one rowboat upside down beside a shack with a sign for bait. The shops were only Judson's General Store and Judson's Gas Station.

A bell jangled as they went into the store. It was dim and cluttered and smelled of dusty bolts of cloth and strong cheese. Behind the counter stood a tall, thin woman who kept her hands in her apron pockets while she looked them over with stern interest.

"Good morning!" their mother said. "I'm Mrs. Coyne. This is my son Filmore and my daughter Jodi. We've rented the Hogarth place."

"Heard you did," said the storekeeper.

"We need milk and a few groceries. Also lumber and nails, if you have them. We'd like to mend the front stoop. You don't think the owner would mind, do you?"

"Not likely. He hasn't seen the place in years. But I'd wait if I were you. See if you like it there, first."

"Don't you think we'll like it?" Filmore asked.

"Been a lot of folks in and out the Hogarth place. City folks, mostly. Like you. They never stay long."

"Because it's run-down, or is there something else?" Filmore asked.

His mother interposed. "Do you happen to know if the chimney works?"

"Did once. Likely needs sweeping."

"Is there someone who might do it for us?"

"Mr. Judson. My husband. He can fix the front stoop, too, if you want. Rehang those shutters. Trim the bushes. You would have to pay, though. The real estate agency won't. Cost you twenty dollars."

"That would be just fine!"

When Mrs. Judson was adding up the prices on a paper bag, Filmore asked, "Why don't people stay long at Hogarth's?"

Mrs. Judson was busy checking her figures.

"Because of what's there besides us," Jodi said. "Isn't that right, Mrs. Judson?"

Their mother looked at Mrs. Judson with a smile, but Mrs. Judson was busy packing groceries.

"But we like it, Mrs. Tiggy-winkle and I. It sounds so beautiful and sad. Especially the little bell."

"What little bell?" Filmore asked.

"Didn't you hear it? It was so sweet last night, going tinkle-clink all around the house."

Mrs. Judson rang up the money with a loud jangle of her register. "Suit you if Mr. Judson comes tomorrow morning?"

Back in the car, Filmore said, "She wasn't very friendly."

"I thought she was," said their mother. "She tried to help us all she could."

"She didn't smile, not once," Filmore said. "And she wouldn't tell us anything."

"That's because she was nervous," Jodi said.

"Why would she be nervous?" their mother asked.

"For us. She thinks we might be afraid in the house."

"But there's nothing to be afraid of!" said their mother.

Jodi laughed. "We know that!"

Early next morning, Mr. Judson arrived in a truck, with toolbox and planks of wood. He too was tall and thin, with the same gaunt face as his wife, but with a tuft of gray beard attached.

All morning while they were on the beach, Filmore could hear Mr. Judson hammering, thumping, and snipping. At noon he came and said, "Chimney's working. I laid a fire. Got to go, now. The missus will be waiting."

They walked with him to his truck. "How do you folks like it here?" he asked, lifting his toolbox into the back.

"We love it!" Jodi answered.

"It's a charming house, really," their mother said. "I wonder why it hasn't been sold?"

"Because of what's here," Jodi said. "Isn't that right, Mr. Judson?"

Mr. Judson was searching among his tools. "Must have left my pliers somewhere, Mrs. Coyne."

"It's a cat," Jodi said.

"A cat, Jodi?" their mother asked. "Are you sure? Is there a cat, Mr. Judson?"

"Never saw one here, myself. Leastwise not in years."

"You mean there used to be a cat?" Filmore asked.

"Mrs. Hogarth, she had one. Hogarth, he moved away when his missus died. Don't know what became of the cat."

"Could it be a neighbor's cat?"

"She has a squeaky little voice," Jodi said. "Probably hoarse from crying."

"Haven't heard tell of any lost cats," Mr. Judson said. He went around to the cab of his truck.

"Could it be a stray?"

"Oh, she's not a stray," Jodi said. "She wears a little rusty bell that goes tinkle-clink when she runs. It's so sweet."

Mr. Judson climbed into his truck and turned on the ignition. "If you find my pliers, will you bring them next time?"

As they watched the truck rattle down the road, Filmore asked, "Don't you think the Judsons act strange? Like they're hiding something?"

"No, dear," his mother said. "I think they're just reticent. That's how people are in this part of the country."

That night, Filmore was awakened by someone shaking his toes. "Filmore! I have to tell you something!"

Jodi was leaning against his bed with Mrs. Tiggy-winkle in her arms. Moonlight falling through the window made her eyes like holes in a mask. "Do you hear the cat?" Jodi whispered. "She's prowling and crying all around the house, now. She wants to come in."

Filmore held his breath to listen. He did in fact hear a wailing and sighing and rustling of leaves. "That's the wind."

"And the cat, too," Jodi insisted.

"All right, get in my bed, if you're scared."

"We're not scared. But we are cold." She climbed on the bed and settled the quilt around Mrs. Tiggy-winkle.

17

Filmore rolled over and closed his eyes. "Go to sleep. There isn't any cat. Mr. Judson said so."

"He did not. He said he never saw a cat, leastwise not in years. But we did."

Filmore turned back. "You saw it?"

"Yes, on the beach this afternoon. She was watching us through the weeds, a yellow cat with red eyes."

"Then why haven't mother and I seen it?"

"Because she's invisible."

"You said you saw it!"

"We did! Mrs. Tiggy-winkle and I! Both of us! First we saw her eyes and then we saw her whole self!"

"You don't even know what invisible means!"

"We do too! It means mostly people can't see her."

"It means nobody ever sees her!"

"But she can fix that when she wants to. Anyway, she is prowling and crying right now. She wants somebody to let her in."

"If she's invisible, she can let herself in!" Filmore cried, triumphantly.

"That's not the same," Jodi said, straightening the quilt.

Filmore turned away. "You make me tired! What did you come bothering me for!"

Jodi sighed and threw off the covers.

"You can stay if you're nervous," Filmore muttered.

"We aren't nervous. But you are! So we'll stay."

At breakfast, Jodi said, through a mouthful of blueberry pancakes, "When you have a cat, you're her mother and daddy, you know, so you must never leave her, like Mr. Hogarth did. That's why she's always crying and prowling and never can rest."

Their mother looked down at them from her pancake griddle.

"We have to put some food out for her, Mother," Jodi said.

"If there's any cat around here, it finds its own food," Filmore said.

"That's right, dear. It got along all right before we came."

"No, she didn't! She's skinny all over and her little bones show! Can't I give her my milk? Please, Mother, please!"

Their mother smiled. "Not your milk, Jodi. We'll find some scraps."

Filmore followed Jodi to the kitchen stoop, where she settled the scraps and a pan of water.

"She's already been here, looking for food," Jodi said. "See her paw prints?"

Filmore bent to examine the stoop. "That's just wet sand. The wind did that. You're putting this food here for nothing. No cat's going to eat it."

"Of course not. She's a ghost. Ghosts can't eat."

"Then why are you putting it here!" Filmore exclaimed, exasperated.

"She doesn't need to eat it, just to have it. To know we love her."

On the beach that afternoon, their mother was reading under the umbrella while Jodi sat beside her on the sand, sorting her beach treasure. Filmore waded for a while, but he felt uneasy by himself and soon came back to flop beside his sister.

The grasses above the beach rattled in the wind. "Is the cat watching us now?" he whispered.

"Oh, not now. The hot sand hurts her feet."

"I thought you said she was a ghost!"

"But she can hurt, just the same."

Later, clouds rolled up over the sea and the wind turned cold. Filmore took down the umbrella while his mother folded the beach chair and they ran for the house through pellets of rain.

That evening Filmore forgot the cat in the pleasure of popping corn over a snappy fire. Their mother sat rocking and mending, and Jodi sprawled on the hearth, humming to Mrs. Tiggy-winkle. Firelight threw quivering shadows on the walls. Outside the rain was like handfuls of sand thrown at the windows.

Filmore glanced at his mother. Her face was thoughtful and withdrawn. Whenever he caught her in such a mood, she would quickly smile, as though to insist she was all right. This time, however, she spoke.

"Remember last summer? Our last vacation with Daddy? Remember the day he bought every balloon the man had, and you three went along the beach and gave them away to children? He wanted us to share our happiness. Remember, Jodi, how happy he wanted us to be?"

"Is it popcorn yet?" Jodi asked. "I don't hear any more pops."

When Filmore passed her the popcorn, she said, "Mrs. Tiggy-winkle feels just the same as me. But not the cat. She hurts. Because she was murdered. That's why she's a ghost."

Filmore saw that his mother's needle had stopped, but she did not look at them.

"When somebody leaves you, they always murder you a little bit. But Mr. Hogarth, he murdered her a lot, until she was dead."

"If you know so much, how did he do it?" Filmore demanded.

"First he starved her and then he drowned her and then he told her she was bad. That's why she's so skinny and wet. She hates to be skinny and wet. She's outside now, crying at the kitchen door. Can't you hear her? She wants to come in by the fire."

"You're daft!" Filmore exclaimed. "That's just the wind!"

"Please, Mother, please! Can't I let her in?"

Their mother gave Filmore a glance that asked for patience. "All right, dear. Let her in."

Jodi rose with Mrs. Tiggy-winkle and went to the kitchen. Filmore heard the kitchen door open and then the screen. A cold draft blew through the room and dashed at the flames on the hearth.

"Hurry up, please!" their mother called. "You're cooling off the house."

21

When Jodi came back, Filmore said, "Well, where is the cat?"

"She can't come in because she knows you don't love her."

"But you and Mrs. Tiggy-winkle love her! Isn't that enough?"

"Can Mrs. Tiggy-winkle have some more popcorn, please?"

When the fire burned low and their mother announced bedtime, Jodi said, "She's crying again, Mother."

"Jodi, dear, why do you upset yourself this way? Can't you just enjoy your vacation with Filmore and me?"

"Yes, but she has to be happy, too! That's why we came here, you know! Can't I let her sleep on my bed tonight?"

Their mother sighed.

"You think I just imagine her, don't you?"

"Of course!" Filmore said. "You are the only one who sees her!"

"I am not! Mrs. Tiggy-winkle sees her, too!"

"And Mrs. Tiggy-winkle isn't real, either!"

"All right, if I just imagine her, why can't I have her on my bed?"

Their mother smiled. "I can't argue with that."

In his room, Filmore heard the squeal and slap of the screen door and then his sister's clumpy steps on the stairs. Straining, he thought he also heard soft paws running up beside her and the tinkle of a bell.

"Now she's got me doing it!" he muttered.

The rain grew quiet, the wind died, waves gently washed the shore. The next time Filmore opened his eyes, it was nearly daylight. He pulled on his robe and went to his mother's room.

"What is it, Filmore?" she asked. Like Jodi, she always woke up at once.

"Let's see if Jodi really has a cat."

He took her hand as they went down the hall. "You don't believe there's a ghost cat, do you?"

His mother stopped in the hall. "Not literally, dear, of course. But Jodi does, so we must try to be understanding. She's still very little, you know. She isn't quite sure where reality stops and the stories of her mind begin."

"But why would she make up this crazy story?"

"We'll have to see if we can think of why."

Jodi's window opened on a huge dark sea and a rosy horizon. The sound of rolling waves was like the breathing of a giant in sleep. Jodi was curled under the quilt, her black hair shining on the pillow and Mrs. Tiggy-winkle under her chin.

"There's no cat!" Filmore whispered. "She made the whole thing up!" He felt an odd mixture of indignation, relief, and disappointment.

Jodi sat up brightly. "We're not asleep!"

"Did you and Mrs. Tiggy-winkle have a good night?" their mother asked.

"Yes, and so did the ghost cat. She stayed right here on my bed till she got warm and dry, and then she went away."

23

To Filmore she added, "If you don't believe me, look at this! She gave me her bell!"

Jodi opened her hand to show him a little rusty bell on a bit of frayed ribbon.

Filmore was going to accuse her of finding the bell on the beach, when he caught his mother's eye.

"Why did the ghost cat leave you?" their mother asked. "Doesn't she love you?"

"Yes, but she had to go because she was dead. Just like Daddy, you know."

Filmore saw his mother's eyes grow cloudy, but she hid them by hugging Jodi. He went and made a circle with them, turning his face away also.

Muffled by their arms, Jodi said, "That's why we're hugging and crying and smiling, right?"

TURQUOISE HORSE

Gerald Hausman

Some years ago, in Navajo country, there was a girl named Lisa Todachine whose father was a silversmith.

When Lisa was twelve years old, she had a dream in which she chased a horse. She was on foot in the dream, and the horse raced ahead of her, dancing on small delicate hooves.

The dream came again and again. During the day Lisa did not think about the dream, nor did she mention it to anyone. But at night, before she went to sleep, she remembered the horse, and it made her sad to think that though she saw the horse every night, her dream was always in black and white.

There came a night when the dream changed into color. Lisa was running along a narrow trail upon a vast mesa and the horse was ahead of her, its mane flashing in the wind, its forehooves striking sparks on the hard-packed earth.

When it happened she was not surprised but pleased. The horse reared magnificently on a rock outcropping, and then, in a blaze of blue it transformed into a turquoise horse. The moment this happened Lisa knew she was in a dream, because in real life there is no such thing as blue horses. And then the horse did a wonderful thing. Rearing over the verge, it suddenly leaped into the open, empty air and, pawing miraculously, found its footing in the sky. Then it whinnied triumphantly and galloped off across the clouds.

The next morning Lisa went to where her father worked on his jewelry behind their hogan. In the warm seasons, summer and fall, he usually did his work under a four-post juniper shelter, the upper latias of which were spindly bark-peeled branches. Shadows fell in clean lines at his feet. He worked in the cool of this outdoor workshop until, little by little, the sun grew bolder and bolder and stole all the way into the shadow of the shelter.

Lisa liked to watch her father work. His composure seemed cast of the same fire-blackened silver as his bracelets, rings, and pins. He was a man of mud and fire, blood and bone whose surface was etched and hammered by years of sun and rain. He knew what it meant to make a mold and what it meant, as a grown man, to have been molded by nature.

Lisa knew that her father was wise. She also knew that he was certain of the old ways that had been taught to him by his own father. From father to son, mother to daughter the teachings came down, year after year, sun after moon.

"Father," Lisa said, "I have a dream to tell you."

She waited while he removed a casting from the hot coals before which, holding iron tongs in a pair of heavy cowhide gloves, he sat back on the heels of his elk moccasins.

"Yes," he said, finally. "Tell me your dream."

"There is a horse. I run after it but I can never catch it. Mostly the horse is dark because I dream this dream in black and white. But last night, for the first time, the horse looked me in the eyes. I heard it snort loudly before it turned turquoise and galloped away into the clouds. Father, I need to know what this dream means, for I have it every night."

Lisa's father said nothing, nor did he look into his daughter's worried face. He bent over his tufa-casting and tapped it with a little hammer.

Lisa knew that her father was not ignoring her. He was not, as it appeared, concentrating only on his work. He was, she knew, thinking deeply about what she had told him.

Then he got slowly to his feet and stretched his arms.

"You get stiff in that position," he said, then, "Come with me for a moment, Lisa."

Together, they walked on the dry wash just below where her father worked. A little ribbon of water, sky-colored, shivered between the clay banks that rose above their shoulders.

After walking for a few minutes, her father stopped.

"I think it was here," he said. "Yes, I am certain of it, here."

"What?" Lisa asked.

"I was your age, maybe a little younger when I made the discovery. Do you see where the water runs down from high up on the hill? Where there is now a dry scar on that cliff?"

Lisa nodded. In rainy times, such soft eroded places sang full-throated with tumbling water. If you were not careful, when the water ran at its fullest, you could be swept to your death.

"When I was your age," Lisa's father began, "I was caught in one of those sudden storms. The whole hillside seemed to come down on my head. I got swept away. A big juniper branch saved my life. I held onto it for all I was worth. When my grandfather pulled me to safety, we both stopped in our tracks. For directly in front of us was a ruined grave, one that the wild waters had ripped apart. There was silver everywhere, for as you know, the dear possessions of the dead are buried with the body."

Lisa's father turned on his moccasined heel and began to walk back to his workshop on the hill above the arroyo.

"What does this mean, Father?" she asked.

"In all that silver, there was a bracelet, that even now after all the years, I remember as if it were yesterday. The silversmith had made that bracelet a hundred years ago, and yet it was as new as the day he measured the wrist that wore it . . . a wrist that was once flesh and bone, a wrist that is now dust."

"What did you do with the bracelet?"

Looking at his daughter for the first time, Lisa's father smiled a little crookedly. She knew what that meant. Trouble. A lesson. She had said something wrong.

"You know it is a bad thing to disturb the sacred places of burial. I did nothing with the bracelet. I merely looked at it. I took it with my eyes, for a moment, and held it there. Then my grandfather and I walked on and we erased that place from our memory. It is only now, as you told me of your dream, that I remembered."

"That gravesite," Lisa said, "was ruined in the rain. You didn't know where the real location of the grave was, only where the jewelry turned up at your feet."

"That is right."

"Then why couldn't you take it and give it a proper home? Otherwise it could've been taken by someone less than yourself, a thief perhaps."

"To take that which does not belong to you, no matter the circumstances, is a bad thing. Let the runner run, the walker walk, and the thief thieve. You can't change that which is—the rain, the run-off, the broken grave. We didn't touch that silverwork. Perhaps it's still there, perhaps not. It doesn't matter. What is important is that we saw the bracelet with our eyes . . . we embraced it. From that moment on, I knew I would be a silversmith."

"But how did you know?"

29

"I knew because I understood—having almost drowned—that only those things which live are worth living for."

Lisa said, "I understand now."

"There is something else," her father said kneeling before his dwindling fire. "The thing that made the bracelet so beautiful was the turquoise horse that decorated it. I've never forgotten that horse that seemed to be dancing on a cloud."

Lisa waited for him to say something more, but he busied himself with his casting.

That night Lisa dreamed the dream of the turquoise horse, and again, she saw it in color. This time the horse danced upon a cloud, just as her father had said, and it beckoned her to follow. She was afraid. Backing away from the edge of the great cliff where the horse had taken its swift leap into the air, she felt fear in her throat.

"I can't come with you," she said to the horse, "I can't walk on air."

Then the horse galloped to the mesa, and kneeling as her father had knelt before the fire, it bowed its head. Lisa had only to take one step and she would be on its back. She hesitated, and then heard the voice that came from the clouds.

The voice said, "The turquoise horse is yours now."

It was a command and Lisa obeyed.

The horse got to its feet and in one graceful bound, tossing its neck to the east, it dropped off the cliff like falling water. Then it flailed its hooves on the air, parted the clouds, swam up into the sky.

Lisa clung to the horse's mane, but she did not feel fearful. Easily, dreamily, like flowing silk, she let the horse have its head. And the horse plunged higher into the cliffs of cloud and was swallowed up.

Then she felt her body melt as the vapors wrapped her round, and the voice of the cloud-person spoke again.

Lisa could see nothing, for the mist was everywhere. She felt the gleaming flank muscle of the turquoise horse. This was real, she told herself, the voice of the cloud-person was real.

Then the world, the universe stood still, the clouds froze and everything turned into still-life.

"Hear me," the cloud-person said, "I am of the family of the Sun. The horse you ride on belongs to us. But we do not own him. No one can own the Turquoise Horse."

Lisa woke with a start. It was morning, the weekend was over and it was time to get dressed for school. The dream she'd been having dissolved in her waking mind. She got dressed, put her books in her bookbag, and had breakfast with her mother and father. They ate in silence. Morning was quiet time. It was not necessary to speak. Instead they listened.

At school Lisa remained quiet. In little bits throughout the morning her dream returned, giving her no peace. It was only after lunch, after she had gone running several miles with her friends, that she realized how tired she was, how her dream had physically drained her.

31

Back in the classroom, her teacher introduced a folksinger, a man with a handlebar mustache who had been assigned to their school district by the Arizona Commission on the Arts. He walked about the room, plunking a banjo and urging the children to write verses of a song that all of them would compose together.

She liked the tune and the verses rolled out, tinkly and funny, and they made her forget her dream. All the students in the room were laughing and the mustached man made his banjo ring: "Put your head on the floor, pick it up, pick it up; put your head on the floor, pick it up, pick it up."

Lisa could not help smiling at this man who was all smiles himself. Although he was not Navajo, there was something Indian about him. He didn't act like a white person. Like her father, he was sure of something. That something was inside the tight white drum head of his banjo.

If only she were sure . . . if only she had something she were certain of . . . the banjo rang for the last time. Then it was time for the students to write their own composition, something of their own, which the mustache-man would put to music for the following day.

Lisa wasn't going to write anything. She doodled on the creamy sheet of paper that covered her desktop. But her doodling, mindless and abstract, changed into something else. She began to draw the turquoise horse. The moment she saw its image drawn by her own hand on paper, she heard the words of the cloud-person.

I am the Sun's son.
I sit upon a turquoise horse
    at the opening
    of the sky.

My horse walks
    on the upper circle
    of the rainbow.

My horse has a sunbeam
for a bridle.

My horse circles
    all the people
    of the earth.

Today, I, Lisa Todachine, ride
upon his broad back
and he is mine.

Tomorrow
he will belong to another.

The drawing and the words came out of her so fast, she didn't have time to think about them. Then they were collected by the folksinger whose name was John Arrowsmith. For a moment, when he came to each desk to pick up the papers, she felt him touch her and his hand was rough as sandpaper, not soft the way she imagined a musician's hand should feel, but hard like her father's.

That night Lisa did not dream. Restlessly, she tossed and turned in her sleep. When morning came, she was unwell. Her father, already out in his workshop by the time she started breakfast, was striking silver with his hammer, and the ting-tang of his hammer made her think of the folksinger named John Arrowsmith. Prickles when she thought of him. Her poem. She was afraid . . . but was it a poem? . . . she did not know.

After breakfast, on her way to the bus stop, Lisa visited her father. He was in that meditative morning mood. Not a good time to disturb him, but she had to.

"Father, I've done a bad thing," she said.

Quickly her father's eyes met her own. Then he looked away, waiting politely for her to speak. He didn't busy himself with his jewelry this time. His hands were folded in his lap, and he waited.

"I dreamed of the turquoise horse," she said gently. "No, I dreamed not of him, I dreamed I was part of him, that I rode him all the way to the top of the sky. There I met a cloud-person who told me that the horse belonged to him. I was permitted to ride the turquoise horse, but it belonged to the family of the sun."

"You've dreamed a great dream, Lisa. You rode the turquoise horse; you've been embraced by the holy people."

He looked awed by this and she burst into tears.

He reached toward her without actually touching her, his hands outstretched, his palms open, asking.

"You don't understand," she sobbed. "Yesterday, a musician came to our class, and I liked his music. I liked him. I liked the way he played his banjo, it made everyone happy.

"This is foolish, I know. That is why I am crying. And because I think I've done a bad thing. The singer asked us to write a poem which he would put to music. I wrote about the turquoise horse. Today, I think he will sing about it, and I am ashamed. This is like taking the silver bracelet from the spoiled grave. I had no right to tell my dream in words and put them on paper. I have stolen from a sacred grave. I am a thief."

As she said these words, her father listened without expression. When she was done, he broke into a smile.

"You have not stolen anything, child. You were given something. A blessed thing that dream was . . . but how you choose to share it is up to you—your decision, and yours alone. Remember, in the dream, the cloud-person said the horse was for all to share."

"But what if he takes my song and sells it and makes money from it. It would be a sin."

Sighing, her father said, "The world's made up of many people. Not all are righteous—but the cloud-person trusted you . . . now you must trust yourself."

That day passed slowly for Lisa. She could hear what people said to her, but they seemed to speak from such a distance, and their voices were almost inaudible. Even on the playground, shouts of her friends came to her in muffled silence. She was waiting, waiting for the moment when he would walk into the room and sing her song. She could hear his banjo ringing, his happy mustached face glowing as he sang her song. But at the same time, regardless of what her father said, she felt the awful shame of the betrayed secret. She wanted to bury her song, to hide it away forever.

At last the moment she'd been anticipating arrived. John Arrowsmith came into the classroom. He took out his banjo and tuned it. Then he spread four pieces of art paper on a desk.

"These are your songs," he said, "and I'm going to sing them for you. Naturally, I wish I had the time to make tunes for all the things you wrote, but I only had one night . . . anyway, here goes . . ."

John Arrowsmith sang four songs, one right after the other. The class loved them. One about a goat that butted everyone; one about a house that flew up to the moon; one with a catchy tune that went—"People these days should be nice to each other, people these days have to care for one another, people these days, people these days . . ."

Lisa didn't hear her song though. He probably hadn't even read it. The hollow feeling inside her got bigger. She was relieved because the secret of the turquoise horse was still a secret. And yet, she was disappointed. . . .

After school, walking toward the bus, she saw John Arrowsmith about to get into his pickup truck. He gave her a big smile and a wave.

"You're Lisa, aren't you?"

She stopped in her tracks as he came over, his leather briefcase in hand. He had on a black cowboy hat with a horsehair hatband. Close up, he was rougher-looking than she thought. Like his hands, he was weathered in the face.

"Did I get your name right?" he asked gently.

"I'm Lisa Todachine."

"Doesn't that name mean bitterwater? If so your father's the silversmith. I'm wearing one of his buckles."

Lisa felt the warmth come around her. She liked him. She was right to have trusted him.

"He's a silversmith, while you are a poet! I didn't sing your song today because I felt it was private, something between you and your family maybe. Well, there's another reason, too. I don't think it's really a song. There may be a fine line of difference between a song and a poem, but I think this is a poem. When you decide to really share it with people, you might think about putting it in a book."

Lisa blushed.

"Well, so long." He handed the poem back to her.

"Poem," she said to herself. What a funny word. What a funny, lovely, feeling-kind-of-word.

When she got back to her home, she put the poem of the turquoise horse on the wall of her room where anyone could see it . . . anyone in her family, that is.

But she knew, because she had changed, that her family was growing. It now included her father and mother, her mother's family and her father's family, a cloud-person and a turquoise horse, a folksinger named John Arrowsmith, and people she had not even met who would one day read her poems in a book.

She was going to have a big family, of that she was sure.

Maurice's Room

Paula Fox

THE COLLECTION

Maurice's room measured six long steps in one direction and five in the other. The distance from the floor to the ceiling was three times higher than Maurice. There was one window through which Maurice could see several other windows as well as a piece of the sky. From the middle of the ceiling dangled a long string, the kind used to tie up packages of laundry. Attached to the end of the string was a dried octopus. It was the newest addition to Maurice's collection. When his mother or father walked into his room—which wasn't often—the octopus swung back and forth a little in the draft.

Maurice had used a ladder to climb up high enough to tack the string to the ceiling. The ladder was still leaning against the wall. Instead of returning it to Mr. Klenk, the janitor of his building, from whom he had borrowed it,

Maurice was using the steps for shelves. Even though Maurice's father, Mr. Henry, had put up a dozen shelves around the room for all of Maurice's things, there still weren't enough.

Maurice knew how to walk around his room without stepping on anything, and so did his friend Jacob. But no one else did.

As his mother and father often said to visitors, it was astonishing how much junk a person could find in one city block. His mother said Maurice kept their block clean because he brought up everything from the street to his room. His father said Maurice ought to get a salary from the Department of Sanitation because of all the work he was doing in cleaning up the city. At least once a month Mr. and Mrs. Henry talked about moving to the country. It would be better for Maurice, they said. But then they would decide to wait a little longer.

Some visitors said that collections like Maurice's showed that a child would become a great scientist. Many great scientists had collected junk when they were eight years old. Other visitors said Maurice would outgrow his collection and become interested in other things, such as money or armies. Some suggested to the Henrys that they ought to buy Maurice a dog, or send him to music school so that his time might be spent more usefully.

In his room Maurice had a bottle full of dead beetles, a powdery drift of white moths in a cup without a handle, a squirrel hide tacked to a board, a snakeskin on a wire hanger, a raccoon tail, a glass of shrimp eggs, a plate of mealy worms, a box of turtle food.

There were things with which to make other things, such as nails of different sizes, screws, wire, butterfly bolts, scraps of wood, sockets, filaments from electric-light bulbs, cardboard from grocery boxes, two orange crates, a handsaw, and a hammer. On the top of a chest of drawers Maurice kept stones and pebbles, dried tar balls, fragments of brick, pieces of colored bottle glass that had been worn smooth, and gray rocks that glistened with mica.

On his windowsill there was a heap of dried moss next to a turtle bowl in which several salamanders lived half hidden by mud and wet grass. On the same sill he kept some plants from the five-and-ten-cent store. They looked dead. Now and then a cactus would put out a new shoot.

In another bowl on a table covered with yellow oilcloth were four painted turtles that were getting quite soft in the shell, and in a corner, in a square fish bowl with a chicken-wire roof, lived a garter snake and a lizard. An old hamster in his cage slept or filled his pouches with dried carrots or ran on his wheel. The wheel, which needed an oiling, screeched all night, the time the hamster preferred for exercise. But the noise didn't keep Maurice awake, only his parents. In a pickle jar, a garden spider sat in a forked twig, her egg sack just below her. Maurice also had a bird. It was a robin, blind in one eye and unable to find food for itself.

On the floor were coffee cans with things in them; an eggbeater with a missing gear, a pile of dead starfish, cigar boxes, clockworks, hinges, and a very large grater with sharp dents on all four of its sides. The grater was orange with rust, and it stood in the middle of the room beneath the octopus. You would have to use a magnifying glass to see all the other things Maurice had found.

His bed had two blankets and a pillow without a pillowcase. Sometimes a small goose feather pricked its way through the ticking, and Maurice would put it away in an envelope. He had used two pillowcases for his collecting expeditions, and after that his mother wouldn't give him any more.

There was one tidy corner in Maurice's room. It was where he had pushed his Christmas toys. They were a month old now, and the dust covered them evenly. They were like furniture or bathroom fixtures. Maurice felt there wasn't much to be done with them.

"GET EVERYTHING OFF THE FLOOR"

It was the end of January, and Maurice had just come home from school. He put his books on his bed and went to see what the snake was doing. It was lying on its rock. The lizard was watching it. The robin was so still it looked stuffed. But it cocked its head when Maurice whistled at it. The hamster was hiding bits of carrot in the sawdust at the bottom of its cage. The salamanders had buried themselves in the mud. Maurice was arranging little piles of food for his animals when he heard his uncle's voice from down the hall.

"Lily," his uncle was saying to his mother, "you ought to dynamite that room!"

"There must be another way," his mother said.

"You'd better give it up," said his uncle. "Maurice will never clean it."

"If we lived in the country, it would be different," said his mother.

"Perhaps," said his uncle.

Maurice took two walnuts from his pocket and cracked them together. His mother came to the door.

"Get everything off the floor," she said in a low, even voice as though she were counting moving freight cars.

"Where will I put things?" asked Maurice.

"I don't care," she said. "But clear the floor! Or else I'll bring in the broom, the dustpan, and a very large box. And that will be that!"

The doorbell rang. It was Jacob.

"Jacob can help you," his mother said.

Jacob was seven, but he looked bigger than Maurice. It was because he was wearing so many clothes—scarves, mittens, sweaters, two hats, and several pairs of socks. He began to take off his outer clothing, laying each item in a pile at his feet. Meanwhile Maurice explained the predicament.

"What are we going to do?" asked Jacob.

Maurice looked at the chest of drawers. The pebbles and rocks had been moved to the floor, and the chest was now covered with oatmeal boxes. He looked at the table. He could barely see the yellow oilcloth because it was hidden by sections of a witch doctor's mask he and Jacob had begun to make the week before. The turtles had been moved next to the salamanders on the windowsill.

"There are five more floors in this room if you count the walls and ceiling," Maurice said to Jacob. Jacob looked smaller and thinner now that he was down to his shirt and pants.

"I see," said Jacob.

"We'll have to ask Mr. Klenk to help us," said Maurice.

Jacob began to sort out nails. Then he stopped. "But we won't be able to do that with everything! And how can we get it all done in just a day?"

"Mr. Klenk will know," said Maurice.

THE JANITOR

Mr. Klenk, the janitor, lived in the basement five floors down. The basement smelled like wet mops, damp cement, pipes, and old furniture stuffing. But it was clean. Mr. Klenk had told Maurice that he couldn't relax a second or he would be drowned by the rubbish that poured out of all the apartments. "Overwhelming!" Mr. Klenk often exclaimed.

"It's a race between me and the junk," he would say. "If I let it get an edge on me, I'll get shoved right out of the city." But Mr. Klenk didn't seem to feel the same way about Maurice's collection.

"Well, you're selective, my boy," he had said once, giving Maurice a caramel. "Besides, I suspect you've got something in mind for all that stuff of yours."

The two boys rang the janitor's bell. Mr. Klenk opened his door, blowing out a cloud of cigar smoke.

"I have to get everything off the floor," Maurice said. "Could you help us a little?"

"What do you have in mind?"

"There's plenty of space on the walls," said Maurice.

Mr. Klenk nodded and puffed on his cigar. "I know," he said. "But you didn't bring back my ladder, did you?"

"He forgot," said Jacob timidly. Mr. Klenk peered through the cigar smoke. Jacob backed away. The janitor in the building where Jacob lived sat in a big collapsed steamer trunk all day just waiting, Jacob was sure, for boys to wander by so he could pounce on them.

"Can you come now?" asked Maurice.

"Let's go," answered Mr. Klenk.

When they reached Maurice's room, Mr. Klenk stopped at the doorway.

"How am I supposed to get in there?" he asked.

Jacob cleared a path for him. Maurice took all the things off the ladder steps, and in a few minutes Mr. Klenk was at work.

First Maurice chose the starfish. He handed it to

Jacob, who held it up to Mr. Klenk on the ladder. Next came the rusty grater. In an hour everything was hanging either from the ceiling or from the walls. The animals paid no attention to the fact that they were suspended above the floor. The hamster went to sleep; his cage swung gently like a hammock in a light breeze.

By six o'clock, the floor boards appeared. It was a good floor, and Maurice and Jacob sat down on it.

"Now we have room for more things," said Maurice.

Maurice's mother and his uncle came to the door.

"Wow!" said Uncle.

Mrs. Henry looked pale. "I didn't have *that* in mind," she said.

"Well, Lily, they've cleared the floor," said the uncle. He looked at Maurice. "I have a surprise," he said. "I'm going to bring Patsy here to spend a week with you."

Then his uncle winked at Mrs. Henry. "You'll see," he said to her. "Patsy will take his mind off all of this." Maurice's mother looked doubtful.

"Who is Patsy?" asked Jacob.

"Who is Patsy!" repeated the uncle, as though astonished. "Tell him, Maurice."

"A dog," said Maurice. "A dumb fat dog," he added in a whisper to Jacob.

After Maurice's uncle and Mrs. Henry went back to the kitchen, Mr. Klenk picked up his ladder and started to leave. Then he seemed to remember something. He tapped Maurice on the shoulder.

"Would you like a stuffed bear?" he asked.

"I'd like a bear," Maurice said.

"A tenant left it when he moved out," said Mr. Klenk. "Send your man down for it in the near future." He nodded at Jacob.

"We could make a car for it," said Maurice after Mr. Klenk had left.

"There's a busted baby carriage in front of my building," said Jacob.

"Bring the wheels," said Maurice.

Jacob began to put on all his outdoor clothes.

"I never heard of a bear having a car," he said.

"Why not?" asked Maurice.

THE DOG

Maurice and Jacob were unable to begin building a car for the bear the next day because Patsy arrived early in the morning.

Patsy was a large soft dog with beady eyes. She was wearing a plaid wool coat. Maurice and she stared at each other for several minutes. She was nearly as tall as he was. Then she walked straight into Maurice's room. When she came out a minute later, she had an oatmeal box in her mouth.

"Give me that!" demanded Maurice. Patsy lowered herself slowly on her four legs until she was lying on the floor with the box in her teeth.

Maurice looked at his mother. She was smiling and nodding. He looked at his father, who was just about to leave for work.

"Nice dog," said his father.

"Give it back," whispered Maurice to Patsy. She stared at him. Then she turned her head suddenly, and Maurice snatched the oatmeal box and ran to his room with it. He closed the door and went back to the kitchen to finish his bacon and cocoa.

When he came out to put on his galoshes before going to school, Patsy was sitting in the living room. She was chewing an ear section of the witch doctor's mask. He ran to her and grabbed it. Patsy stood up and wagged her tail. Maurice could see she was just waiting for him to leave. He pretended to go to the front door, then suddenly turned and tiptoed back to his room. Patsy was already in it, sniffing up at the hamster.

"Please leave my room," said Maurice. Patsy looked at him over her back. He slipped his fingers beneath her collar and pulled. It was difficult to drag such a big dog. His mother came to the door. "Don't bully the dog," she said. "Good Patsy!"

"I don't want her in my room," said Maurice.

"She's so friendly," his mother said. Patsy wagged her tail and sat down on Maurice's foot.

"She was trying to eat the hamster," Maurice said.

"Oh!" exclaimed his mother. "You're exaggerating! She was only looking around. She probably misses your uncle."

Maurice looked at a round hole in his door near the knob where he and Jacob had dug out the lock and the latch months ago.

"Couldn't we put the lock back in?" he asked.

"Not now," said Mrs. Henry. "Now you go to school. You're going to be late!"

Right after his arithmetic class, Maurice asked the teacher for permission to go to the principal's office. The secretary said he could use the telephone for two minutes.

"Hello," said Maurice's mother.

"Is she in there?" asked Maurice.

"Who?" asked Mrs. Henry.

"Pull the octopus higher," said Maurice.

"Oh, Maurice," said Mrs. Henry, "as if I didn't have enough to do! Patsy doesn't want your octopus."

Maurice looked up at the clock.

"Can't you tie her to something?" Maurice asked.

"Stop fussing," said Mrs. Henry.

After school, Maurice ran all the way home. He was out of breath when he reached his front door.

Patsy was lying asleep in the living room. Maurice's things were all around her like a fortress. Her head was resting on the raccoon tail.

It took Maurice an hour to put everything back. Patsy watched him from the door.

"Thief!" he said to her. She wagged her tail.

The next day Maurice did not feel very well. His mother said he could stay home provided he kept to his bed. "None of this wandering around in bare feet," she said.

Maurice was happy to stay in his room. He watched Patsy as she paced back and forth outside his door. When she tried to sneak in, he shouted, "No, you don't!"

That afternoon he heard his mother speaking with his uncle on the telephone.

"Maurice and Patsy are inseparable," she said. "You were quite right. We must get him a dog of his own."

"A whole week," said Maurice to himself. He began to feel really sick. Suddenly Patsy made a dash for the chest of drawers. She put one paw on a drawer pull.

"Out!" shouted Maurice, standing up in the middle of his bed with the blankets flapping around him. Patsy ran from the room, but she sat down right in front of the door.

The next day Maurice felt poorly again. His mother took his temperature. He had no fever. His throat wasn't red. But his eyes looked strained. The strain came from staring through the dark at Patsy half the night. But the dog had fallen asleep before Maurice had, and so she had been unable to steal a single thing from Maurice's room.

"I think you should go to school," said Mrs. Henry.

"No!" said Maurice, kneeling on his bed.

"Mercy! You don't have to kneel," she said. "What *is* the matter?"

"I can't go to school," Maurice said.

Mrs. Henry called Mr. Henry.

"I think he is developing a school phobia," Maurice heard her say to his father as they stood in the hall outside his room.

At that moment, Patsy raced in, threw herself at the bed, snatched a blanket, and made off with it. Maurice jumped to the floor and ran after her. They both slammed into Maurice's father.

"If you don't stop playing with Patsy, I'll have to send her home!" said Mr. Henry.

After that, it was easy. Maurice played with Patsy every minute he could, and soon his uncle came to get her. He dressed Patsy in her plaid coat, clipped on her leash, put on his hat, and left.

"You see?" said Maurice's father.

Maurice nodded.

THE BEAR

One Saturday morning, a few weeks after Patsy had left, Maurice awoke at six o'clock. His window was blurred because it was raining so hard. The hamster stirred in its cage.

"You're up too early," Maurice said. The robin lifted one wing slowly and opened its good eye. Maurice went into the kitchen and made himself a grape-jelly sandwich. It felt good to be eating a sandwich and walking down the hall so early in the morning. No one else was awake. He gave a piece of bread crust to the robin and one to the hamster. Then he got dressed.

Soon there was a soft knock on the front door. It was Jacob, who always arrived early on Saturday mornings and who usually brought something with him. Today he was carrying a paper sack.

"Do you want a jelly sandwich?" asked Maurice. Jacob nodded. Then he showed Maurice what he had brought in the bag.

"What is it?" asked Maurice.

"I think it's for weighing things. I found it in a box on the street," Jacob said, holding up a large white scale. The paint was chipped, and when Maurice pressed his hand down on the platform, the needle on the dial jiggled.

"Your arm weighs six pounds," said Jacob.

Maurice's mother walked by. She was yawning. She glanced into the room. "Good morning, children," she said.

"My arm is very heavy," said Maurice.

"That's nice," said Maurice's mother, and yawned again and walked on.

"I forgot to tell you," Jacob said. "Mr. Klenk said to come and get the bear."

Maurice put the scale on his bed. Then both boys ran to the front door and down the five flights of stairs to Mr. Klenk's room in the basement. Mr. Klenk was blowing on the cup of coffee he was holding in one hand. He still carried a broom in the other.

"It seems I hardly have time for coffee," said Mr. Klenk. "I'll be glad to get rid of that bear."

He left them standing at the door, peering into his room. There was so much cigar smoke in the air, it was hard to see the furniture. In a minute Mr. Klenk was back, pushing the bear before him. The bear's feet were strapped into roller skates. It was as tall as Jacob.

"Here he is," said Mr. Klenk. "Think you can handle him?"

Jacob and Maurice stared. The bear was plump. Its fur was black. Its two front paws stuck out straight in front of it. The claws were of different lengths, and some of them pointed upward as though the bear had been pushing against a wall.

"Why is it wearing skates?" asked Maurice.

"It came that way," said Mr. Klenk.

"It looks tired," said Jacob.

"It had a long sea voyage, all the way from South America."

Maurice pulled and Jacob pushed and they got the bear up the stairs all the way to Maurice's front door, and inside. Because of the skates the bear moved easily on a level surface, but it had been a slippery business getting it up the stairs.

"I think we'd better wait a while before we show it to my mother and father," said Maurice. "They don't like surprises."

"Mine neither," Jacob said.

Maurice said, "Why don't you get your hat and coat and put them on the bear and maybe they'll think it's you if we push him down the hall fast."

Jacob went to get his outdoor clothes. They dressed the bear, pulling Jacob's hat almost all the way down its muzzle. Then, running, they propelled it down the hall. As they went by his parents' bedroom, Maurice's father poked his head around the door.

"Who's that?" asked Mr. Henry in a sleepy voice.

"Jacob!" said Maurice.

"Maurice!" said Jacob.

Mr. Henry went back to bed. "You shouldn't roller-skate in the house," he said.

At last they got the bear into a corner of Maurice's room. "The bear has a funny smell," said Jacob.

"You're right," said Maurice. "But we'll have to get used to it."

They took Jacob's clothes off the bear. Then they stood and looked at it. It was pleasant to have a big animal in the room with them, even if it was stuffed.

"Maurice," Mrs. Henry called. "Come and drink your apple juice."

"We'll have to disguise it. Then one day when they're feeling good I'll just tell them I have a bear," said Maurice in a whisper. Then he called out, "We'll be there in a minute."

"Couldn't we hide it under the bed for a while?" asked Jacob.

"No," said Maurice. "It won't fit because the Victrola's there. But wait a minute." Maurice opened his closet door and pulled out a heap of clothing. Pretty soon he found what he wanted. It was a penguin costume.

"It was for Halloween," said Maurice.

They started dressing the bear. They had to cut holes in the feet to fit the costume over the bear's roller skates. Then they zipped up the front and pushed the bear between the table and the window. Nothing was left showing of it except the big bumps where its paws were.

Then they went to the kitchen and had apple juice and doughnuts.

PATSY AGAIN

The next day, which was Sunday, Maurice's uncle was coming to visit. When Maurice heard that Patsy was coming with him, he went to his room and began to pile up things behind his door.

Maurice's father knocked, and Maurice opened the door a crack.

"Maurice," he said, "you'll have to clean out the hamster's cage. There's a very strong smell coming from your room."

"All right," said Maurice. "I'll do it right now."

He looked at the bear in its penguin costume.

"I wonder if I could spray you with perfume," he said.

Then he took a piece of rope and tied one end of it around the bear's neck and the other to his bedpost. If somebody came in, he decided, he would just roll the bear out the window and then pull it back into the room when the coast was clear.

A few minutes later, he heard his mother let his uncle in at the front door.

"Well, Lily, how are you?"

"Fine, and you?"

"Fine, and your husband?"

"Fine, and Patsy?"

"Fine."

"Fine," said Maurice to the hamster.

"And how is Maurice?" asked the uncle.

"Fine," said his mother.

"He'll be delighted to see Patsy."

"He surely will be delighted."

Maurice added his boots to the heap behind his door.

A large object suddenly hurtled down the hall and against Maurice's door. It was Patsy. The barricade gave way, and Patsy raced into the room, stomping and huffing and panting. The snake slid under its rock, the lizard froze, the hamster burrowed in its sawdust, and the bird closed its good eye.

Patsy stopped dead in her tracks. Maurice stood up slowly from where he had been crouching near his bed. Patsy's nose was in the air. She was sniffing. She slid one floppy paw forward, then another. Maurice sprang toward the bear, his arms outstretched.

"Don't lay a hand on that bear!" he cried.

It was too late. Patsy leaped. Over and down crashed the bear. All eight wheels of the roller skates spun in the air. Patsy sat on the bear and began to bay. Maurice could hear his mother, his father, and his uncle racing down the hall.

He ran to the window, flung it open, and deposited the turtles on the floor. He grabbed a blanket from his bed and threw it over Patsy, who fell into a tangled heap alongside the bear. In a flash, Maurice had the bear up on its skates and on the sill. He gave it a shove, and out it went through the window, the rope trailing behind it.

Mr. Klenk, who was sweeping the courtyard below and whistling softly to himself, heard the whir of spinning roller skates and looked up.

"Ye gods!" he cried. "A giant penguin!"

THE TRUMPET LESSON

"Today you are going to start your trumpet lessons," said Mrs. Henry. She held out a black case that reminded Maurice of a crocodile's head. Maurice put it on his bed and opened it. The trumpet glittered. He could see his face reflected in it.

He looked out of his window. A light rain was falling, a March rain that might be warm. It was exactly the kind of Saturday Maurice and Jacob liked to spend hunting for new things for the collection.

"You'll have to leave very soon," said Mrs. Henry as she started back to the kitchen to finish her cup of coffee. Maurice lifted the snake out of its cage. The snake wound itself around his wrist. It was a dull green color and quite small.

"The trouble with you is you don't have enough interests," he said to the snake. He put it back in its cage and pulled the chicken wire over the top. Then he put on his light jacket.

When he got to the front door, his mother said, "Just a minute. Haven't you forgotten something?" She was holding out the trumpet case. "And Maurice, really! It's raining! Put on your rubbers and your heavy jacket."

"Maurice, you must learn to be more responsible," said his father, who was standing at the other end of the hall eating a piece of whole-wheat toast.

Maurice went back to his room, dug into his closet, and found one of his rubbers and one of Jacob's. He wished he had been born wearing one pair of shoes and one suit of clothes.

Jacob was waiting for him in front of the building.

"Do your lessons really start today?" he asked.

"Yes," said Maurice. As he had guessed, it was a warm spring rain.

"Will you have to go every Saturday morning?"

"For six weeks," said Maurice. "Then they'll see."

"See what?" asked Jacob.

"If I get new interests."

On their way to the music school where Maurice was to take his lesson, they passed a big junkyard. A sign hung over the wire fence that surrounded the yard: *Auto Parts*. A man wearing a hat was walking around the piles of bumpers and tires and car bodies. Now and then he would kick an old fender.

"Why don't you wait for me in there," Maurice suggested. "Maybe you can find something good." The man with the hat walked into a little house not much bigger than a telephone booth. There was a small window in it. Maurice could see the man fiddling with a radio.

"Maybe he'll chase me away," said Jacob, looking at the man.

"I'll stay for a minute," said Maurice.

They walked toward the rear of the lot. The man looked out of his window but didn't seem to see them. He was chewing on a toothpick and still twisting the radio dials. Just behind the little house, Maurice and Jacob could see the long arm of a crane.

"Look at that!" said Maurice, pointing to a pyramid of heaped-up car parts. Poking out of the pile were hubcaps, fenders, tires, fan belts, radiator caps, pipes, window frames, steering wheels on shafts, and at the very top, lying on a car hood, a pair of headlights that looked almost new.

"We could use those headlights," said Maurice.

Jacob looked back at the little house. "He won't give them to us," he said.

"Maybe he'd make a trade," said Maurice.

"What could we trade?" asked Jacob.

"We'll think of something," Maurice answered. "But first we have to see those headlights."

"How will we get them?" asked Jacob.

"Climb," said Maurice. "See all the places you can put your feet?"

"Me?" asked Jacob.

"I think you can do it better. I'm heavier. If I tried it, everything might crash down," Maurice said.

"Are you going to ask him first if we can?" asked Jacob.

"He's not even looking at us," said Maurice.

Jacob put his right foot on a tire rim, then grabbed hold of the fender above him and brought his left foot up to another tire. Slowly he climbed toward the top, using the tires as steps.

Suddenly there was a loud clanging of metal, then bangs, screeches, and a crash. When the dust cleared, Maurice saw Jacob almost at the top of the pyramid, stretched out on a silver-colored car hood, clutching its sides.

The man ran out of his little house. When he saw Jacob, he threw his hat on the ground.

"What's the meaning of this!" he shouted.

"We'd like to make a trade," said Maurice.

"Trade! At a time like this?" bellowed the man. "Get off my property!"

"Help!" said Jacob in a weak voice.

"How will we get him down?" asked Maurice.

59

The man picked up his hat and jammed it back on his head. "Can't he fly?" he growled; then he turned and walked to the crane. He jumped up to the seat and began to push the levers around furiously.

"Don't worry," Maurice called up to Jacob. "He's going to get you down."

Jacob didn't answer. He wasn't scared now, and he rather liked being so high above the ground.

There was a grinding of gears and a maniacal roar as the man maneuvered the crane into position.

"Clear away," shouted the man to Maurice. Maurice ran back toward the little house and watched as the claw at the end of the cables lowered its jaw, then clamped onto the hood where Jacob lay, gripped it, and lifted it down slowly like a plate. Several tires dislodged by the crane rolled along the ground.

"Well, get up," said Maurice to Jacob. Jacob was feeling sleepy. He shook himself a little and stood up.

"How was it?" asked Maurice.

"Okay," said Jacob.

The man jumped down from the crane, picked up a tire, and kicked it so hard it rolled all the way back to the pile. Then he started toward them.

Maurice and Jacob hurried to the gate. But Maurice stopped suddenly and darted into the little house, where he placed the trumpet on top of the radio.

"It's too late for my lesson anyhow," he said to Jacob as the man yelled after them, "I've got a friend on the police force!"

On the way home, Jacob said, "What will your mother and father say?"

"Plenty!" said Maurice.

A BIRTHDAY PRESENT

In a few weeks Mr. and Mrs. Henry stopped mentioning the trumpet. After that, whenever Maurice happened to hear them, they were talking about moving to the country. "We'll have to move anyway, at the rate Maurice is going," Mrs. Henry said once. "If he puts one more thing in his room, he won't have a place to stand."

But Mr. Henry wanted to wait.

On a morning late in April, Mrs. Henry brought Maurice a glass of fresh orange juice on a little tray. There was a sign leaning against the glass. It read: "Happy Birthday to Maurice." She couldn't get into the room, so Maurice got up from his bed and went to the door to get the tray.

Jacob came at noon and they had a birthday lunch. Maurice blew out all of his nine candles but he forgot to make a wish. Then Mr. and Mrs. Henry brought in a large box.

Maurice looked inside. It was a three-foot-long sailboat. The rigging was made of cord. The sails were of canvas, the winches really turned, and the hatches could be taken off and put back. It had two masts.

"It's a ketch," said Maurice's father, who was sitting on the floor next to him. "Look at those lines! Some boat!"

"Will it really sail?" asked Jacob.

"It will," said Mr. Henry.

"Can we take it to the lake right now?" asked Maurice.

"Yes," said Mr. Henry. "But be very, very careful with it."

Maurice's mother smiled. "It's nice to see you so interested in something," she said to Maurice.

The two boys carried the boat to the park. They dropped their jackets on the grass and sat down on the cement ledge that ran all around the lake. Then they rigged the sails.

A brisk wind was blowing. Maurice and Jacob slid the boat into the water. Instantly, it raced toward the center of the lake, its sails puffed out with wind. The boys ran around to the other side, but Jacob suddenly stopped. His hair was blowing almost straight up.

"Come on!" shouted Maurice.

"Look!" said Jacob, pointing at the water. Two or three feet out from the shore, something glistened as the breeze lifted the water into small waves.

"Bedsprings," said Maurice.

"How can we get them?" asked Jacob.

Maurice sat down on the ground and took off his shoes and socks, but Jacob waded in after Maurice with his shoes on. The springs were heavy, and weeds were growing through them.

They dragged them onto the grass. Maurice put on his shoes and socks and jumped on the springs.

"We can borrow wire cutters from Mr. Klenk and make coils to put on our shoes."

"We can hook it up so it stretches across the room," said Jacob.

"I can pull it across the door so Patsy doesn't get through," said Maurice.

They picked up the springs and started home. Jacob's wet shoes squeaked.

Then Maurice stopped. "We forgot something," he said.

They dropped the springs and ran back to the lake. On the opposite side was the boat, its stern halfway up the cement ledge, its sails flapping.

"What are you going to tell them?" asked Jacob as they lifted the boat out of the water. The stern was smashed and the mainmast tilted.

"I don't know yet," answered Maurice.

"Could we say there was a little storm?"

"No, we'll have to tell them what really happened— that the boat went out of control," said Maurice.

"Because we weren't watching," said Jacob.

They put the boat on top of the springs; then with Maurice holding the front of the springs and Jacob the back, they started home.

At first, Maurice's father didn't say anything. Mrs. Henry told Jacob to go home and change his wet socks and shoes; then she went to the kitchen. Maurice heard her rattling pots and pans.

"If I had known you wanted bedsprings instead of a beautiful three-foot sailing ketch, I would have gotten you bedsprings," said Mr. Henry at last.

Maurice said nothing.

"Go to your room and think about what happened," said Mr. Henry.

Maurice put the sailboat under his bed next to the Victrola so he wouldn't have to look at it. He put a blanket on the bedsprings and sat down on them. One of the coils had come loose and was bobbing up beside him. He rested his arm on it.

He heard his parents talking the rest of the afternoon. His mother brought him a supper tray while it was still daylight.

Then Mr. Henry came and stood in Maurice's doorway. Maurice was still sitting on the springs.

"I have something to tell you," he said. "We have decided to move to the country as soon as school is over."

"How will I see Jacob?" asked Maurice.

"Jacob can take the bus. It's not very far. You can have a dog."

"Not Patsy!" asked Maurice.

"No," answered his father. "But your uncle has a racing bike he is going to give you. It's a little old, but it still goes."

"I'm sorry about the boat," said Maurice.

"Your mother and I are sorry too," said Mr. Henry. He came over and sat down next to Maurice on the bedsprings.

"They're still a little damp," he said.

Maurice gave him a corner of the blanket to sit on. They didn't speak about the sailboat. In fact, it was never mentioned again.

AN EXPLOSION

The Henrys moved to the country the day after school ended. Mrs. Henry said Maurice could take his collection if he could find something to pack it in. Mr. Klenk gave him an old steamer trunk with broken hinges. Jacob brought a length of rope to tie around it. Maurice was able to get everything into the trunk except the bedsprings. He gave them to Jacob.

The movers' truck drew up in front of Maurice's building around noon. Mr. Klenk, Jacob, and Maurice stood outside and watched the movers load the furniture on.

"I don't see how they can get all those things into the truck," said Jacob.

"They fit them together like a jigsaw puzzle," said Mr. Klenk.

The last items the movers brought down were Maurice's animals and his trunk. They placed the cages on top of bureaus at the front of the truck. They left the trunk at the back, near the tailgate.

"Can I ride in the truck with my things?" Maurice asked his father.

"If it's all right with the movers," said Mr. Henry.

Mr. Klenk waved his cigar at Maurice. "Come back and visit me," he said. "I'll keep an eye out for interesting things for your collection."

Jacob didn't say goodbye. He was coming out to visit the next day. He waved as Maurice hiked himself up onto the truck.

All the way through town, Maurice could see his mother and father driving behind in the rusty jeep they had bought for the country. But soon he lost sight of it as the truck pulled ahead.

Maurice walked to the front, winding through the furniture and crates, the boxes and baskets, to check up on his animals. The hamster was running on his wheel, but the robin, the snake, the lizard, and the salamanders were all asleep.

They turned off on a blacktop, then onto a dirt road. After that, the ride got bumpier. There were no buildings, no gasoline stations, no signs—only green hills and trees and birds sitting on telephone wires. Here and there a crumbling stone wall followed the curve of a hill. The sun was very warm, and the canvas curtains on either side of the truck's tailgate flapped back and forth.

All at once, there was a tremendous crash. The furniture rattled, the cages danced on top of the bureaus, the robin chirped, and the pots banged against each other. They had driven over a big bump. Maurice's trunk teetered as they rounded a curve, then flew out, hit a rock, and seemed to explode into the air. Maurice saw his collection flying in all directions, then drop out of sight down the hill.

The truck stopped just as the jeep arrived. Maurice's father came running up to Maurice and lifted him down. Then everyone went to look over the hill. Maurice's things lay scattered everywhere among the rocks and tall grass. Maurice sat down on the road.

Mrs. Henry knelt beside him.

"Wow!" said Maurice. "Did you see that?"

Mrs. Henry stood up.

"The whole trunk blew up!" said Maurice. "It flew out in the air and exploded!"

"You can start a new collection," said Mr. Henry.

But Maurice didn't hear him. He was thinking that even the paper sacks of water he and Jacob had once dropped from the roof to the courtyard hadn't made such a terrific noise. He had never seen anything like it.

MAURICE'S BARN

Maurice's new room had one window and a slanted ceiling that was so low that Mr. and Mrs. Henry couldn't stand up straight beneath it.

When Maurice awoke the morning after the move, a branch was tapping against the windowpane and there were leaf-shaped shadows on the floor. Maurice wondered if he could step from the window to the big round branches of the tree that stood just outside. Just beyond the tree, Maurice could see a red barn. As he stared at it, a flock of birds flew from under the barn roof, circled in the sunlight, and flew back.

The room was empty except for Maurice's animals and his suitcase and the bed. The fields outside seemed empty too, except for the tall grass. The house was silent.

In the kitchen Maurice found a package of saltines and a glass of milk he had been too tired to finish the night before after all the unpacking.

Maurice's father walked in and sat down at the table. It was the same one that had been in Maurice's room in the city.

"Did you see the pump?" asked Mr. Henry.

"What's that?" asked Maurice.

"Sometimes there are storms, and the electricity goes off. Then you can use the hand pump to get water. It's just outside the door."

Maurice poked his finger into a little hole in the oilcloth.

"What do you think of the country?" asked Mr. Henry.

"It's okay," said Maurice.

"You are making a large hole in the oilcloth, Maurice. Why don't you take a look outside? Have you been to the barn?"

Maurice tried to balance four saltines against one another.

"Jacob will be here soon," said Mr. Henry. "You can take him to see the stream."

"What's in it?" asked Maurice.

"All right, Maurice," his father said, "you know what's in a stream!"

Maurice ate half a saltine. He wasn't very hungry.

"You'll get used to it here," said Mr. Henry. "It's new now. But you'll find lots of things to interest you."

At the word *things*, Maurice looked up at his father.

"There's nothing but grass," he said.

"Take a look in the barn," said Mr. Henry.

On his way out, Maurice tried the pump. He had to use both hands. Nothing happened for a moment; then a stream of cold bluish water gushed out on his sneakers. He squashed his way through the tall grass and the brambles to the barn.

The biggest door was padlocked, but next to it was a small door which hung half open from one hinge. He slipped inside.

He heard a great rustling of wings. For a moment he stood still, waiting for his eyes to get used to the dark. Then he looked straight up. The roof of the barn seemed miles above him. Small birds swooped through the rafters from which hung spider webs as big as trapeze nets. As soon as Maurice began to walk, an interesting musty smell arose from the floor. On his right were wooden stalls and on his left was an old hay wagon. One of its big wheels lay on the floor, half covered with hay. There were ladders of all sizes leaning up against the walls, and from the posts that supported the overhead rafters hung an extraordinary assortment of objects.

"Fish nets," said Maurice aloud. "A hoe, a rake, a bucket, another bucket, a bamboo pole with a line and three fish hooks, a dog collar, mousetraps, a leather jacket, a pitchfork, a lantern." There were many other things made out of leather or wood or metal, but he didn't know what they were.

A big shaft of sunlight fell across the floor. Maurice turned and saw his father standing in the doorway. Bits of hay and dust floated around him.

"Your mother has gone to get Jacob at the bus stop," he said.

Maurice noticed several lengths of chain and a tire tube hanging from a nail near the door.

"Do you like the barn?" asked Mr. Henry.

"Yes," said Maurice.

"That's where they used to keep the hay," said Mr. Henry, pointing to a platform above the wagon. "But I don't think we're going to have cows or horses." Just then Jacob came to the door. He was carrying a paper bag.

"Come in and see my barn," said Maurice.

Jacob stepped inside.

"What's in the bag?" asked Maurice.

"Jelly doughnuts and a wrench Mr. Klenk gave me to give to you."

Maurice cleared the hay off the rim of the wagon wheel, and they sat down to eat their doughnuts.

"Your mother said there was a stream we could fish in," said Jacob.

"Not yet," said Maurice. "We have to fix up this barn. We have to find out what's in it. We can repair things. Like this wheel. We'll put it back on the wagon. Then, when we get too hot, we can go to the stream."

"What do we do first?" asked Jacob.

"First we have to find out the name of everything," said Maurice.

"Why?" asked Jacob.

"Because that's how you begin," answered Maurice. "Okay?"

"Okay," said Jacob.

BARBIE

Gary Soto

The day after Christmas, Veronica Solis and her baby sister, Yolanda, nestled together on the couch to watch the morning cartoons. Bumbling Inspector Gadget was in trouble again, unaware that the edge of the cliff was crumbling under his feet. Soon he was sliding down the mountain toward a pit of alligators. He commanded, "Go, go, gadget umbrella," and a red umbrella popped out of his hat. He landed safely just a few feet from a dark green alligator and dusted himself off.

Veronica liked this show, but she was really waiting for the next one: "My Little Pony." That show had lots of Barbie commercials and Veronica was in love with Barbie, her blond hair, her slim waist and long legs, and the glamorous clothes on tiny hangers. She had wanted a Barbie for as long as she could remember and almost got one last Christmas, but her Uncle Rudy, who had more money than all her other uncles combined, bought her the worst kind of doll, an imitation Barbie.

Veronica had torn the silver wrapping off her gift and found a black-haired doll with a flat, common nose, not like Barbie's cute, upturned nose. She had wanted to cry, but she gave her uncle a hug, forced a smile, and went to her bedroom to stare at the doll. A tear slid down her cheek.

"You ugly thing," she snapped and threw the imposter against the wall. The doll lay on the floor, eyes open like the dead. Immediately, Veronica felt ashamed. She picked up the doll and set it beside her.

"I'm sorry. I don't hate you," she whispered. "It's just that you're not a *real* Barbie." She noticed that the forehead was chipped where it had struck the wall, and that one of the eyelashes was peeling off like a scab.

"Oh, no," she gasped. Veronica tried to push the eyelash back into place, but it came off and stuck to her thumb. "Doggone it," she mumbled and returned to the living room, where her uncle was singing Mexican Christmas songs.

He stopped to sip from his coffee cup and pat Veronica's hand. "Did you name your doll yet?"

"No, not yet." Veronica looked at the floor. She hoped that he wouldn't ask her to bring it out.

"Let's see her. I'll sing her a song," he teased.

Veronica didn't want him to see that the doll's face was chipped and one of her eyelashes was gone.

"She's asleep," she said.

73

"Well, in that case, we'll let her sleep," he said. "I'll sing her a lullaby, 'Rock-a-Bye-Baby' in Spanish."

That was last year. There had been no Barbie this Christmas either. Today was just a cold, winter morning in front of the television.

Her Uncle Rudy came over to the house with his girlfriend, Donna. Veronica's mother was uneasy. Why was the girlfriend here? Was this the moment? She dried her hands on a kitchen towel and told the children to go play outside. She turned to the woman and, ignoring her brother, asked, "What'd you get for Christmas?"

"A robe and slippers," she said, looking at Rudy, then added, "and a sweatsuit from my brother."

"Come, have a seat. I'll start coffee."

"Helen, would you call Veronica back inside?" Rudy asked. "We have an extra present for her."

"OK," she said, hurrying to the kitchen, her face worried because something was up and it could be marriage. She called, "Veronica, your uncle wants you."

Veronica dropped her end of the jump rope, leaving her sister and brother to carry on without her. She walked back into the house and stood by her uncle; but she couldn't take her eyes off the woman.

"How's school?" asked her uncle.

"Fine," she said shyly.

"Getting good grades?"

"Pretty good."

"As good as the boys? Better?"

"Lots better."

"Any *novios*?"

Donna slapped Rudy's arm playfully. "Rudy, quit teasing the child. Give it to her."

"OK," he said, patting Donna's hand. He turned to Veronica. "I have something for you. Something I know you wanted."

Uncle Rudy's girlfriend reached in a package at her feet and brought out a Barbie doll in a striped, one-piece swimsuit. "This is for you, honey."

Veronica stared at the woman, then at the doll. The woman's eyes were almost as blue, and her hair almost as blond as Barbie's. Veronica slowly took the Barbie from the woman and very softly said, "Thank you." She gave her uncle a big hug, taking care not to smash Barbie against his chest. Veronica smiled at the woman, then at her mother, who returned from the kitchen with a pot of coffee and a plate of powdery-white donuts.

"Look, Mom, a Barbie," Veronica said happily.

"Oh, Rudy, you're spoiling this girl," Mrs. Solis chided.

"And that's not all," Rudy said. "Donna, show her the clothes."

The woman brought out three outfits: a summer dress, a pants suit, and a lacy gown the color of mother-of-pearl.

"They're lovely!" said the mother. She held the summer dress up and laughed at how tiny it was.

"I like them a lot," said Veronica. "It's just like on TV."

The grownups sipped their coffee and watched Veronica inspect the clothes. After a few minutes Rudy sat up and cleared his throat.

"I have something to say," he said to his sister, who already suspected what it was. "We're getting married—soon."

He patted Donna's hand, which sported a sparkling ring, and announced a second time that he and Donna were getting married. The date wasn't set yet, but they would have their wedding in the spring. Veronica's mother, feigning surprise, lifted her eyes and said, "Oh, how wonderful! Oh, Rudy—and Donna." She kissed her brother and the woman.

"Did you hear, Veronica? Your uncle is going to get married." She hesitated, then added, "To Donna."

Veronica pretended to look happy, but she was too preoccupied with her new doll.

In her bedroom Veronica hugged her Barbie and told her she was beautiful. She combed Barbie's hair with a tiny blue comb and dressed her in the three outfits. She made believe that Barbie was on a lunch date with a girlfriend from work, the fake Barbie with the chipped forehead and missing eyelash.

"Oh, look—boys!" the ugly doll said. "They're so cute."

"Oh, those boys," Barbie said coolly. "They're OK, but Ken is so much more handsome. And richer."

"They're good-looking to me. I'm not as pretty as you, Barbie."

"That's true," Barbie said. "But I still like you. How's your sandwich?"

"Good, but not as good as your sandwich," the ugly doll answered.

Veronica was eager to make Barbie the happiest person in the world. She dressed her in her swimsuit and said in a fake English accent, "You look smashing, my child."

"And who are you going to marry?" the fake Barbie asked.

"The king," she announced. Veronica raised Barbie's movable arms. "The king is going to buy me a yacht and build me a swimming pool." Veronica made Barbie dive into an imaginary pool. "The king loves me more than money. He would die for me."

Veronica played in her room all afternoon, and the next day called her friend Martha. Martha had two Barbies and one Ken. She invited Veronica to come over to play Barbies, and play they did. The three Barbies went to Disneyland and Magic Mountain and ate at an expensive restaurant where they talked about boys. Then all three took turns kissing Ken.

"Ken, you kiss too hard," Martha giggled.

"You forgot to shave," whined Veronica.

"Sorry," Ken said.

"That's better," they said, laughing, and clacked the dolls' faces together.

But at the end of the day the two girls got into an argument when Martha tried to switch the Barbies so she would get Veronica's newer Barbie. Veronica saw that

Martha was trying to trick her and pushed her against the bureau, yelling, "You stupid cheater!" She left with her three outfits and Barbie under her arm.

At the corner she hugged and kissed Barbie. "That's the last time we're going to her house," said Veronica. "She almost stole you."

She sat on the curb, dressed Barbie in her pants suit, then walked through an alley where she knew there was an orange tree. She stopped under the tree, which was heavy with oranges the size of softballs, and swiped one.

As she walked home she peeled the orange with her polish-chipped nails and looked around the neighborhood. With her Barbie doll pressed under her arm, she was happy. The day was almost over, and soon she and Barbie would be sitting down to dinner. After she finished the orange, she wiped her hands on her pants and started to play with Barbie.

"Oh, it's a beautiful day to look pretty," Barbie said. "Yes, I'm going to—"

Veronica stopped in midsentence. Barbie's head was gone. Veronica waved her hand over the space where a smile and blond hair had been only a few minutes ago.

"Darn it," she hissed. "Her head's gone."

She fell to one knee and felt around. She picked up ragged leaves, loose dirt, and bottle caps. "Where is it?" She checked the leaf-choked gutter and raked her hand through the weeds along a fence. She slowly retraced her steps into the alley, desperately scanning the ground. She looked at the headless Barbie in her hand. She wanted to cry but knew it would just make her eyes blurry.

"Where are you?" Veronica called to the head. "Please let me find you."

She came to the orange tree. She got down and searched on all fours, but found nothing. She pounded the ground with her fists and burst into tears.

"She's ruined," Veronica sobbed. "Oh, Barbie, look at you. You're no good anymore." She looked through her tears at Barbie and got mad. How could Barbie do this to her after only one day?

For the next hour she searched the street and the alley. She even knocked on Martha's door and asked her if she had seen Barbie's head.

"No," Martha said. She kept the door half-closed because she was afraid that Veronica was still mad at her for trying to switch their Barbies. "Did you lose it?"

"It just fell off. I don't know what happened. It was brand-new."

"How did it fall off? "

"How do I know? It just fell off. Stupid thing!"

Veronica looked so distressed that Martha went outside and helped her look, assuring Veronica that together they would find the head.

"One time I lost my bike keys at the playground," Martha said. "I just looked and looked. I just got on my knees and crawled around. Nobody helped me. I found them all by myself."

Veronica ignored Martha's chatter. She was busy parting weeds with her hands and overturning rocks and boards under which the head might have rolled. After a while Veronica had a hard time concentrating and had to keep reminding herself what she was looking for. "Head," she said, "look for the head." But everything became jumbled together. She stared at the ground so long that she couldn't tell an eggshell from a splintered squirt gun.

If only it could talk, wished Veronica, who was once again on the verge of tears. If only it could yell, "Over here, I'm here by the fence. Come and get me." She blamed herself, then Martha. If they hadn't had that argument, everything would have been all right. She would have played and then returned home. She probably jinxed her Barbie when she pushed Martha against the chest of drawers. Maybe that was when Barbie's head had come loose; she had been holding Barbie while she fought Martha.

When it began to get dark Martha said she had to go. "But I'll help you tomorrow if you want," she said.

Veronica puckered her mouth and shouted, "It's all your fault! You made me mad. You tried to cheat me. My Barbie was more beautiful than yours, and now see what you've done!" She held the headless Barbie up for Martha to see. Martha turned away and ran.

That night Veronica sat in her room. She felt that she had betrayed Barbie by not caring for her and couldn't stand to look at her. She wanted to tell her mother, but she knew Mom would scold her for being a *mensa*.

"If only I could tell Uncle Rudy's girlfriend," she said. "She would understand. She would do something."

Finally, Veronica dressed in her nightie, brushed her teeth, and jumped into bed. She started reading a library book about a girl in New York City who had lost her cat, but tossed it aside because the words on the page meant nothing. It was a made-up story, while her own sadness was real.

"I shouldn't have gone," said Veronica, staring at the ceiling. "I should have stayed home and played by myself."

She sat up and tried to read again, but she couldn't concentrate. She picked at a scab on her wrist and tried to lull herself to sleep with sad thoughts. When she couldn't stand it anymore, she kicked off the blankets and walked over to her Barbie, which lay on a chest of drawers. She picked up the fake Barbie, too.

"Let's go to sleep," she whispered to both dolls, and carried them lovingly to bed.

Lenny's Red-Letter Day

Bernard Ashley

Lenny Fraser is a boy in my class. Well, he's a boy in my class when he comes. But to tell the truth, he doesn't come very often. He stays away from school for a week at a time, and I'll tell you where he is. He's at the shops, stealing things sometimes, but mainly just opening the doors for people. He does it to keep himself warm. I've seen him in our shop. When he opens the door for someone, he stands around inside till he gets sent out. Of course, it's quite warm enough in school, but he hates coming. He's always got long, tangled hair, not very clean, and his clothes are too big or too small, and they call him "Flea-bag." He sits at a desk without a partner, and no one wants to hold his hand in games. All right, they're not to blame; but he isn't, either. His mother never gets up in the morning, and his house is dirty. It's a house that everybody runs past very quickly.

But Lenny makes me laugh a lot. In the playground he's always saying funny things out of the corner of his mouth. He doesn't smile when he does it. He says these funny things as if he's complaining. For example, when Mr. Cox the deputy head came to school in his new car, Lenny came too, that day; but he didn't join in all the admiration. He looked at the little car and said to me, "Anyone missing a skateboard?"

He misses all the really good things, though—the School Journeys and the outing. And it was a big shame about his birthday.

It happens like this with birthdays in our class. Miss Blake lets everyone bring their cards and perhaps a small present to show the others. Then everyone sings "Happy Birthday" and we give them bumps in the playground. If people can't bring a present, they tell everyone what they've got instead. I happen to know some people make up the things that they've got just to be up with the others, but Miss Blake says it's good to share our Red-Letter Days.

I didn't know about these Red-Letter Days before. I thought they were something special in the post, like my dad handles in his Post Office in the shop. But Miss Blake told us they are red printed words in the prayer books, meaning special days.

Well, what I'm telling you is that Lenny came to school on his birthday this year. Of course, he didn't tell us it was his birthday, and, as it all worked out, it would have been better if Miss Blake hadn't noticed it in the register. But, "How nice!" she said. "Lenny's here on his birthday, and we can share it with him."

It wasn't very nice for Lenny. He didn't have any cards to show the class, and he couldn't think of a birthday present to tell us about. He couldn't even think of anything funny to say out of the corner of his mouth. He just had to stand there looking foolish until Miss Blake started the singing of "Happy Birthday"—and then half the people didn't bother to sing it. I felt very sorry for him, I can tell you. But that wasn't the worst. The worst happened in the playground. I went to take his head end for bumps, and no one would come and take his feet. They all walked away. I had to finish up just patting him on the head with my hands, and before I knew what was coming out I was telling him, "You can come home to tea with me, for your birthday." And he said, yes, he would come.

My father works very hard in the Post Office, in a corner of our shop; and my mother stands at the door all day, where people pay for their groceries. When I get home from school, I carry cardboard boxes out to the yard and jump on them, or my big sister Nalini shows me which shelves to fill and I fill them with jam or chapatis—or birthday cards. On this day, though, I thought I'd use my key and go in through the side door and take Lenny straight upstairs—then hurry down again and tell my mum and dad that I'd got a friend in for an hour. I thought, I can get a birthday card and some cake and ice cream from the shop, and Lenny can go home before they come upstairs. I wanted him to do that before my dad saw who it was, because he knows Lenny from his hanging around the shops.

Lenny said some funny things on the way home from school, but you know, I couldn't relax and enjoy them properly. I felt ashamed because I was wishing all the time that I hadn't asked him to come home with me. The bottoms of his trousers dragged along the ground, he had no buttons on his shirt so the sleeves flapped, and his hair must have made it hard for him to see where he was going.

I was in luck because the shop was very busy. My dad had a queue of people to pay out, and my mum had a crowd at the till. I left Lenny in the living room and I went down to get what I wanted from the shop. I found him a birthday card with a badge in it. When I came back, he was sitting in a chair and the television was switched on. He's a good one at helping himself, I thought. We watched some cartoons and then we played "Monopoly," which Lenny had seen on the shelf. We had some crisps and cakes and lemonade while we were playing; but I had only one eye on my "Monopoly" moves—the other eye was on the clock all the time. I was getting very impatient for the game to finish, because it looked as if Lenny would still be there when they came up from the shop. I did some really bad moves so that I could lose quickly, but it's very difficult to hurry up "Monopoly," as you may know.

In the end I did such stupid things—like buying too many houses and selling Park Lane and Mayfair—that he won the game. He must have noticed what I was doing, but he didn't say anything to me. Hurriedly, I gave him his birthday card. He pretended not to take very much notice of it, but he put it in his shirt, and kept feeling it to make sure it was still there. At least, that's what I thought he was making sure about, there inside his shirt.

It was just the right time to say goodbye, and I'm just thinking he can go without anyone seeing him, when my sister came in. She had run up from the shop for something or other, and she put her head inside the room. At some other time, I would have laughed out loud at her stupid face. When she saw Lenny, she looked as if she'd opened the door and seen something really unpleasant. I could gladly have given her a good kick. She shut the door a lot quicker than she opened it, and I felt really bad about it.

"Nice to meet you," Lenny joked, but his face said he wanted to go, too, and I wasn't going to be the one to stop him.

I let him out, and I heaved a big sigh. I felt good about being kind to him, the way you do when you've done a sponsored swim, and I'd done it without my mum and dad frowning at me about who I brought home. Only Nalini had seen him, and everyone knows she can make things seem worse than they are. I washed the glasses, and I can remember singing while I stood at the sink. I was feeling very pleased with myself.

My good feeling lasted about fifteen minutes; just long enough to be wearing off slightly. Then Nalini came in again and destroyed it altogether.

"Prakash, have you seen that envelope that was on the television top?" she asked. "I put it on here when I came in from school."

"No," I said. It was very soon to be getting worried, but things inside me were turning over like clothes in a washing machine. I knew already where all this was going to end up. "What was in it?" My voice sounded to me as if it was coming from a great distance.

She was looking everywhere in the room, but she kept coming back to the television top as if the envelope would mysteriously appear there. She stood there now, staring at me. "*What was in it?* What was in it was only a Postal Order for five pounds! Money for my school trip!"

"What does it look like?" I asked, but I think we both knew that I was only stalling. We both knew where it had gone.

"It's a white piece of paper in a brown envelope. It says 'Postal Order' on it, in red."

My washing machine inside nearly went into a fast spin when I heard that. It was certainly Lenny's Red-Letter Day! But how could he be so ungrateful, I thought, when I was the only one to be kind to him? I clenched my fist while I pretended to look around. I wanted to punch him hard on the nose.

Then Nalini said what was in both our minds. "It's that dirty kid who's got it. I'm going down to tell Dad. I don't know what makes you so stupid."

Right at that moment I didn't know what made me so stupid, either, as to leave him up there on his own. I should have known. Didn't Miss Banks once say something about leopards never changing their spots?

When the shop closed, there was an awful business in the room. My dad was shouting-angry at me, and my mum couldn't think of anything good to say.

"You know where this boy lives," my dad said. "Tell me now, while I telephone the police. There's only one way of dealing with this sort of thing. If I go up there, I shall only get a mouthful of abuse. As if it isn't bad enough for you to see me losing things out of the shop, you have to bring untrustworthy people upstairs!"

My mum saw how unhappy I was, and she tried to make things better. "Can't you cancel the Postal Order?" she asked him.

"Of course not. Even if he hasn't had the time to cash it somewhere else by now, how long do you think the Post Office would let me be Sub-Postmaster if I did that sort of thing?"

I was feeling very bad for all of us, but the thought of the police calling at Lenny's house was making me feel worse.

"I'll get it back," I said. "I'll go to his house. It's only along the road from the school. And if I don't get it back, I can get the exact number of where he lives. *Then* you

can telephone the police." I had never spoken to my dad
like that before, but I was feeling all shaky inside, and all
the world seemed a different place to me that evening.
I didn't give anybody a chance to argue with me. I ran
straight out of the room and down to the street.

My secret hopes of seeing Lenny before I got to his
house didn't come to anything. All too quickly I was
there, pushing back his broken gate and walking up the
cracked path to his front door. There wasn't a door
knocker. I flapped the letter box, and I started to think
my dad was right. The police would have been better
doing this than me.

I had never seen his mother before, only heard about
her from other kids who lived near. When she opened
the door, I could see she was a small lady with a tight
mouth and eyes that said, "Who are you?" and "Go away
from here!" at the same time.

She opened the door only a little bit, ready to slam it
on me. I had to be quick.

"Is Lenny in, please?" I asked her.

She said, "What's it to you?"

"He's a friend of mine," I told her. "Can I see him,
please?"

She made a face as if she had something nasty in her
mouth. "LENNY!" she shouted. "COME HERE!"

Lenny came slinking down the passage, like one of
those scared animals in a circus. He kept his eyes on her
hands, once he'd seen who it was at the door. There
weren't any funny remarks coming from him.

She jerked her head at me. "How many times have I told you not to bring kids to the house?" she shouted at him. She made it sound as if she was accusing him of a bad crime.

Lenny had nothing to say. She was hanging over him like a vulture about to fix its talons into a rabbit. It looked so out of place that it didn't seem real. Then it came to me that it could be play-acting—the two of them. He had given her the five pounds, and she was putting this on to get rid of me quickly.

But suddenly she slammed the door so hard in my face I could see how the glass in it came to be broken.

"Well, I don't want kids coming to my door!" she shouted at him on the other side. "Breaking the gate, breaking the windows, wearing out the path. How can I keep this place nice when I'm forever dragging to the door?"

She hit him then, I know she did. There was no play-acting about the bang as a foot hit the door, and Lenny yelling out loud as if a desk lid had come down on his head. But I didn't stop to hear any more. I'd heard enough to turn my stomach sick. Poor Lenny—I'd been worried about my mum and dad seeing him—and look what happened when his mother saw me! She had to be mad, that woman. And Lenny had to live with her! I didn't feel like crying, although my eyes had a hot rawness in them. More than anything, I just wanted to be back at home with my own family and the door shut tight.

Seeing my dad's car turn the corner was as if my dearest wish had been granted. He was going slowly, searching for me, with Nalini sitting up in front with big eyes. I waved, and ran to them. I got in the back and I drew in my breath to tell them to go straight home. It was worth fifty pounds not to have them knocking at Lenny's house, never mind five. But they were too busy trying to speak to me.

"Have you been to the house? Did you say anything?"

"Yes, I've been to the house, but—"

"Did you accuse him?"

"No. I didn't have a chance—"

They both sat back in their seats, as if the car would drive itself home.

"Well, we must be grateful for that."

"We found the Postal Order."

I could hardly believe what my ears were hearing. *They had found the Postal Order.* Lenny hadn't taken it, after all!

"It wasn't in its envelope," Nalini was saying. "He must have taken it out of that when he was tempted by it. But we can't accuse him of screwing up an envelope and hiding it in his pocket."

"No, no," I was saying, urging her to get on with things and tell me. "So where was it?"

"In with the 'Monopoly' money. He couldn't put it back on the television, so he must have kept it in his pile of 'Monopoly' money, and put it back in the box."

"Oh."

"Mum found it. In all the commotion after you went out she knocked the box off the chair, and when she picked the bits up, there was the Postal Order."

"It's certainly a good job you said nothing about it," my dad said. "And a good job I didn't telephone the police. We should have looked very small."

All I could think was how small I had just felt, standing at Lenny's slammed door and hearing what his mother had said to him. And what about him getting beaten for having a friend call at his house?

My dad tried to be cheerful. "Anyway, who won?" he asked.

"Lenny won the 'Monopoly,'" I said.

In bed that night, I lay awake a long time, thinking about it all. Lenny had taken some hard punishment from his mother. Some Red-Letter Day it had turned out to be! He would bear some hard thoughts about Prakash Patel.

He didn't come to school for a long time after that. But when he did, my heart sank into my boots. He came straight across the playground, the same flappy sleeves and dragging trouser bottoms, the same long, tangled hair—and he came straight for me. What would he do? Hit me? Spit in my face?

As he got close, I saw what was on his shirt, pinned there like a medal. It was his birthday badge.

"It's a good game, that 'Monopoly,'" he said out of the corner of his mouth. It was as if he was trying to tell me something.

"Yes," I said. "It's a good game all right."

I hadn't got the guts to tell him that I'd gone straight home that night and thrown it in the dustbin. Dealings with houses didn't appeal to me anymore.

THE PRINCE
AND THE GOOSE GIRL

Elinor Mordaunt

Once there was a great Prince who was so great a fighter that no one dared to deny him anything that he asked, and people would give up their houses and lands, their children, and even their own freedom rather than offend him. Everything the people had was his at the asking, they feared him so, and would all tremble and shake when he came thundering past on his war horse, whose hoofs struck great pieces of their fields from the earth as he passed, and whose breath was fire. And they feared his sword, which was so sharp that it wounded the wind as it cut through it, and his battle-ax that could cut the world in half—or so they said—and his frown that was like a cloud, and his voice that was like thunder—or so they said.

Only Erith, the goose girl, feared him not at all.

"He is only a man," she would say. "What you tell of his sword and his battle-ax and his great frown is all a child's tale. He is just a man. He eats and sleeps like other men; if you wounded him, he would bleed. Someday he will love a woman and be her slave for a while just as any other man is. I wouldn't give that for the great bully!" she added, and snapped her little fingers.

"Hee, hee, Erith, that's all very well," the folk would say. "Wait till you meet him thundering over the common. You will fly as quick as any of your geese, we wager."

"I wouldn't move. It's a man's place to make room for a lady, not a lady's place to make room for a man. I wouldn't move, I tell you." And Erith stamped her little foot. It did not seem to impress the village people much, perhaps because it was bare and made no noise on the soft, dusty road, and one needs to make plenty of noise in this world if one is to be noticed.

"A lady! A lady!" they shrieked. "A lord to make place for a lady! Listen to her. My Lady Goosey Gander! A fine lady indeed, with bare feet and no hat."

"There's lots that have shoes that are not ladies," said Erith. "Shoes won't make one, nor bare feet mar one. I'm a better lady than any of you, though, for I'd not run away for anyone, even that ugly old Prince. Bah! He's not noble or good or brave; he's just ugly—an ugly great bully!"

"Wait a bit, Lady Goosey Gander, wait a bit. If ever you see him, you will forget all your fine tales. Why, he's as tall as the church."

"And as strong as the sea."

"Why, his hands are like oak trees."

"And he cares no more than death who he attacks."

"Neither do I care," said Erith, setting back her shoulders and tossing her chin. "All men are babies, anyhow!"

The village gasped. That she should dare! She, a chit of a goose girl, to talk of the terror of the whole countryside like that. "All men are babies!" Well, well!

"It's a good thing that you are only what you are, my girl," growled the blacksmith. "For if you were of any account and the Prince heard what you said, I would not give a farthing for your life."

"Hee, hee, Lady Goosey Gander," hooted the children from that day as they passed her on the way to school, tending her geese up on the common; but she only laughed at them, for she was really and truly brave, you know, and really truly brave people do not trouble much about trifles.

One day one of the Prince's men heard the children and asked Erith what they meant.

"They call me Lady Goosey Gander because I said I was as good a lady as the Prince is a gentleman, and better, for I know enough to be civil and kind," answered Erith, quite unconcerned, busy peeling a willow wand with her little bone-handled knife. She wove these willow wands into baskets while she watched her geese, and sold them in the neighboring market town, for she was poor and had her old mother to keep. She did not stop her work as she spoke; it was more important to her than all the gentlemen or all the Princes in the world. She wanted a bag of meal, and she wanted shoes before the winter began. That was her business; other people might attend to their own.

The gentleman was amused. He told his fellows at supper that night and there was much laughter over the goose girl's words. A page waiting at table told his fellows. And then the Prince's own man told him as he helped him off with his armor that night.

The Prince laughed a great, big, bellowing laugh, but the red swayed up into his face angrily all the same.

"Where does this chit live?" he demanded.

The manservant shrugged his shoulders. "No one knows where she lives; she is of so little importance she might well live nowhere. But she feeds her geese each day on the common above the cliffs to the east, between here and the sea. A barefooted, common little thing."

"There's one thing uncommon enough about her. She dares to say what she thinks about me, and that's more than any of you do. I hear that she is very ugly, though."

"Most terribly ugly, Your Highness," answered the man.

"And old," said the Prince.

"Very old, Your Highness. Quite, quite old."

"And deaf, too."

"As deaf as a post, Your Highness. It's evident she has never heard what all your subjects say about you," agreed the man, for he always did agree—he was too frightened to do anything else.

"It is too evident she *has* heard," said the Prince grimly. "And she is not deaf."

"Oh, no, Your Highness."

"And she is young."

"Indeed the merest child, Your Highness."

"And beautiful."

"As beautiful as the day, Your Highness."

"Only a country girl, of course, quite uneducated."

"Quite uneducated, Your Highness, and—"

What else he was going to say remained unsaid, for he was stooping over the Prince's foot unbuckling his spurs while he spoke, and the Prince lifted his foot—quite easily as it seemed—and with it lifted the man, quite easily, but with such force that he bumped against the ceiling, "plump!" and then came to the floor, "bump!"

There were several other men in the room. However, they did not run to pick him up—they were too frightened of their master. But the Prince just put out the toe of his other foot and touched him, and he rolled over and over like a ball and down the stairs, limpitty, limpitty, limp.

Then another came forward to undo the other spur, and he was treated the same.

"Take them both out and bury them!" shouted the Prince. "And if they're not dead, bury them all the same!" Then he got up and flung around his chamber. He touched no one, but they all fled like hares.

After that he sat down in his great chair, bellowing for wine, and forbade any to go to bed or to sleep, while he sat there himself all night, railing at his men for cowards and fools, and drinking good red wine.

Next morning, directly it was light, the Prince ordered his horse, Sable, to be brought around, mounted it, and rode like the wind to the common by the sea.

"That chit of a goose girl is as good as dead," remarked his manservant as best he could for a broken jaw; indeed, you never saw anything so broken; all his legs and arms seemed nothing but splints and bandages. However, it was a common enough sight in the court of that Prince, and no one took much notice.

The Prince thundered along on his great black horse and presently came to the common. In the middle of it he saw a flock of white geese and a patch of faded blue, which was the smock of the goose girl, who was sitting on a bundle of willow rods, busy with her basket-making.

The Prince did not draw rein. He thundered straight on. He scattered the geese in every direction. He would have galloped right over the girl if his horse had not swerved just as its hoofs were upon her. Then he drew rein.

The girl's hands did not stop from her work, but her great blue eyes were straight upon the Prince's fierce black ones.

"The beast is less of a beast than the master," she said, for she knew it was the horse that had refused to tread upon her.

The Prince pulled his reins, rode back a little, then spurred forward at Erith; but again the horse swerved and, being held with too tight a hand to turn, reared back.

The girl was right under his great pawing black hoofs. But she laughed.

The horse dropped to earth so close that his chest was against hers, his head held high to escape striking her. The foam dropped from his bit; his eye seemed all fire.

The girl's face looked up like a flower from among the thick blackness of his flowing mane. And she laughed again.

This was more than the Prince could stand. He stooped from his saddle. He put his great hand into the leather belt of Erith's smock and swung her up in front of him. There he held her with one hand in its iron glove, shook Sable's rein, and put his spurs to his side.

"I have a mind to ride over the cliff with you," said the Prince.

"Ride over," laughed Erith. And she took the willow rod that was still in her hand and smote the horse's neck with it. "Over the cliff, brave horse, and a good riddance of a bad man it will be," said she.

But the horse swerved at the edge of the cliff. And the Prince let him swerve. Then they turned and they raced like the wind, far, far.

"Are you afraid?" said the Prince.

"Afraid!" laughed the girl. She leaned forward along the neck of the horse, caught one little hand around its ear and cried, "Stop!"

Sable stopped so suddenly that his black mane and long black tail flew out like a cloud in front of him.

The Prince swore a great oath and smote him, but he did not move.

Then Erith, not willing to see him hurt, whispered, "Go!" And he went—like the wind.

Far, far and fast he went. The Prince was brooding too savagely to heed where they were being carried, so that when at length they came to a swamp, the horse, with one of his mighty strides, was borne far into it and sank to his girths before his rider knew what was happening.

You may picture it. The man and the maid and the horse nearly up to their necks in black mud.

Erith was small and light as a bird. She sprang from the arms which were loosed to pull the reins; she caught at a tuft of grass here, at a shrub there, and in a moment was on dry ground, though black to the knees with mire.

But the Prince was a tall, great man. He was all in his armor, very heavy, and he could not move except downward; but he flung himself from his horse.

"That's not so bad of him," thought Erith. "He cares to save it, for he himself would have a double chance on its back."

The fierce black eyes of the man and the laughing blue eyes of the goose girl met across the strip of swamp. His were as hard as steel, for he did not mean to beg his life from any such chit.

Erith moved away a little. "She is going to leave me," he thought, and grieved, for he did not wish to die.

The girl had disappeared among a group of trees, but in a moment she came back, dragging after her a large, thick bough. Then she picked her way cautiously, as near as possible to the edge of the swamp. A little sturdy tree was growing there. Erith undid her leather belt, pressed her back firmly against the tree, and strapped the belt around both it and herself. Then she stretched forward with the bough in both hands.

"Pull," she cried. And the Prince pulled.

The little tree creaked and strained. The goose girl's face grew crimson. It seemed as if her arms must be pulled from her body; but she held on, and at last the Prince crawled out.

Erith had only been muddied a little above her smock, but the Prince was mud up to his armpits, and his face, too, was smeared where he had pushed his helmet back from his forehead with muddy hands. He said no word of thanks to the girl, for he felt that he looked a poor thing, and it made him angry.

"I would I had left you there," said the goose girl. "A thankless boor! You were not worth saving."

The Prince said no word, but began to pull out his horse. Even then the maid had to help him, for it was very heavy and deeply sunk.

Once the horse was free, the maid moved over to a pool which lay at the edge of the swamp and began to bathe her feet and legs and wash the mud from the hem of her smock.

The Prince got on his horse, with a great deal of clatter and grumbling, but she did not turn. They were many, many miles from home, the country was strange and wild, but there she sat, quite untroubled, paddling her feet in the water.

The Prince put his spurs to his horse and galloped away. But the beast would not go freely, spur it as he would. And soon he gave in, let it turn, and so back to the goose girl.

She had dried her feet on the grass by now and was standing plaiting her long hair, eyeing herself in the pool and singing softly.

The Prince drew rein close to her and stuck out one foot. "You may come up," he said.

"An' may it please you," corrected the goose girl very quickly, with her blue eyes full upon him.

"May it please you," repeated the Prince with a wry smile at himself; and the maid put her foot on his and jumped lightly to the saddle before him.

Sable needed no spur then, but sprang into a light gallop.

"All this is mine," said the Prince boastfully, waving his arm as they went.

"I would it belonged to a better man," answered the goose girl. "And sit quietly or I will have no comfort riding with you."

"And you belong to me also," said the Prince savagely.

"Not I. I belong to myself, and that is more than you do."

"What do you mean by that?"

"No man belongs to himself who is the slave to evil temper and pride," answered Erith gravely and gently.

After a long ride they came to the common again. On the edge of it was a tiny cottage.

"Stop here," said the goose girl, "and I will get down."

But the Prince clapped his spurs to his horse's side and they were off like the wind. Moreover, he held the goose girl's hands so tightly that she could not touch Sable's ear or lean forward and speak to him. And so they galloped on till they clattered over the drawbridge into the courtyard of the castle.

A curious couple they looked. The Prince all caked with mud, the goose girl with her wet smock clinging around her bare ankles and her long yellow hair loose, hanging below her knees.

The Prince did not get off his horse, but sat like a statue while all the lords and ladies, the captains and the men-at-arms, the pages and the servingmen—even down to the scullery boy—thronged on the terrace and steps and at every window to look.

There was a long silence. Then one lady, who thought she was pretty enough to do as she liked, tittered loudly.

"The Lady Goosey Gander," she said. "The Lady Goosey Gander."

The Prince's brow grew like a thundercloud. He flung his reins to one of the waiting grooms and alighted, then gave his hand to Erith, who leaped down as lightly as a bird. Still holding her hand, he turned to his people.

"You are always wishing me to choose a wife," he thundered. "Well, I have chosen one, and here she is. You can call the parson to bring his book and get the wedding feast ready, for I will be married in an hour's time."

With that he pulled off his helmet and flung around to kiss the goose girl, but—

"Shame on you," she cried, "to think to marry a maid before you've asked her! You can marry the cat, for all I care." And with that she caught him a great blow across the face and flung free.

Such a slap, such an echoing, sounding slap. The people of the court did not wait to see what would happen, for they knew what the Prince was like in one of his rages all too well, and fled into the palace like rabbits to their burrows—not even a face at the window was left. Only the goose girl did not run, but stood and laughed at the Prince's reddened face.

He caught at her wrist, yet not roughly. "You *will* marry me!"

"Perhaps someday when you learn to speak civilly," she replied. And, feeling her wrist free, she marched off over the drawbridge and over the meadow across the common and so home. She had her own business to attend to.

Some of the Prince's people came creeping back. "Shall we go after her, Your Highness?" they asked, thinking to get into his favor again; but he drove them from him with the flat of his great sword and with oaths and shouting, then flung off to his own chamber and sat there drinking red wine till the night was near over; and none of his court as much as dared to go to bed till he slept.

Next morning he was off again at dawn on his black horse across the common. There sat Erith among her geese, weaving baskets. The very horse neighed with joy at the sight of her sitting there in the sunshine, but the Prince only scowled.

"Will you marry me?" said he.

"No," said she, "and that's flat—not till you learn manners, at least."

Then he got off his horse and took out his sword and killed all her geese.

"You will have to marry me now or starve, for you have lost all your means of getting a living."

But the girl only laughed and took the dead geese and began plucking them, moving over to the side that the wind blew toward the Prince, so that the feathers flew and stuck all over his armor in every chain and crevice and crack; and threw such handfuls of down in his face that when he went to seize her he was powerless.

Next day Erith, having trussed the plucked geese, took them to the market and sold them for a gold piece.

As she came home singing, she met an army of men bearing osier rods. "What have the osiers done that they should all be cut in one day?" she asked.

"The Prince sent us to cut them, Lady Goosey Gander," they answered, jeering. "There is not one left at the brook's edge now, and your basket-making is spoiled."

But the goose girl only laughed and turned back to the town and bought wool with her gold piece.

Next day as she sat before the fire in her cottage spinning the wool into yarn to sell at the market, the Prince came striding in at the little door, bent half double, for it was so low and he so tall with his helmet on his head.

"It is only old women who remain with covered heads in the house," said the goose girl. "Good morning, old dame."

The Prince took off his helmet. Somehow her ways pleased him, for he was sick of soft speaking.

"Will you marry me?" said he.

"When you kneel to ask me," said she. "Not before."

Then in a rage he took all her yarn, flung it into the fire, and was out of the house and away, thundering on his great black horse. But the goose girl only laughed.

Then she took a pair of scissors and cut off her long hair, yellow as honey in the comb, and fine as silk. This she spun and wove into a scarf, the rarest scarf ever seen.

On the third day, having finished her work, she was up at dawn and walked off to the court of a King, many miles distant. There she sought the Queen and sold her the scarf for twenty pieces of gold.

"But why did you cut off your beautiful hair?" asked the Queen.

"It was just forever in the way," replied the goose girl. She told no tales. To begin with, she did not like them, and to end with she *did* like the Prince—perhaps because he was as fearless and obstinate as she herself.

Passing through the town, she bought a bag of meal and porridge. "The bag will do to cover my bare poll when it rains," she said to the merchant, and laughed. The gold jangled in the pocket of her petticoat and she felt as gay as a cricket.

On her way back she met the Prince, who pulled up his horse and scowled at her, that she might not see the love in his eyes. Her head was all over little golden curls that shone in the sunlight.

"What have you done with your hair?" he asked.

"What have you done with the osiers and the feathers?" she asked in return, and laughed.

"Are you starving yet?"

"Far from it. I am richer than I ever was," and she shook her pocket till all the gold danced, for she feared nothing. But it was a foolish thing to do, for in a moment he had whipped out his sword and cut the pocket clean from the petticoat.

"Now will you marry me?" he asked, and held the pocket high and rattled the gold.

"Not I," she said, "if you are so poor that you'd have to live on your wife's earnings." And went her way singing.

The Prince was ashamed of himself. He had never felt like it before, and it was very uncomfortable; it made him feel all tired and hot. It was all the goose girl's fault, of course, and he was very angry. But still he wished he had not stolen her money, and the thought of her little shorn head with its dancing curls made him feel for the first time in his life that he had a heart, and that it hurt.

So wrapped in his shame was the Prince and sitting on his horse so loosely, and so heedless of everything that some robbers coming along the road took courage at the sight of him, for he did not look at all terrible as he usually did, and the gold rattled pleasantly. They had passed him many times before and kept their distance; but now they were emboldened to fall upon him, and so sudden was the attack that he was cast from his horse, the gold was gone, and he bound and gagged before he had thought to resist. Such a poor thing can shame make of any one of us.

Before they had finished, Sable had galloped away. "Shall we ride after him?" asked one of the robbers.

"No, no," answered the others. "He is too well known and we should surely be caught." So they mounted their horses and went off, leaving the Prince bound and more ashamed of himself than ever. But Sable had galloped straight to the goose girl's cottage and struck at the door with his hoof.

When Erith opened the door, she was amazed to see the horse without his master. He muzzled his soft nose over her neck and hand, then trotted a little distance, then neighed as if to call her and returned. This he did several times.

"There must be something wrong," thought the girl; and she put her foot in the stirrup and leaped to the saddle. "Go like the wind," she whispered, leaning along his neck with one little hand around his ear. And like the wind he went.

Now, the robbers had not much rope to spare, so they had bound the Prince kneeling with his arms pulled back and tied to his ankles behind him. And mighty uncomfortable it was. Besides, they had stuck one of their own foul handkerchiefs in his mouth and tied another across and around it. "Anyone who finds me will make a fine mock of me," thought the Prince. And he seemed to burn with rage and shame.

But when the goose girl drew up beside him, *she* did not laugh, rather gave a little moan of pity, for the robbers had struck him wantonly over the head and the blood which he could not reach to stanch ran down over his face and eyes.

In a moment she was to the ground, had whipped out the little knife which she still carried in her belt, and cut the bandage and drew the gag from his mouth. She was turning to the ropes around the wrists and ankles then, when—"Stop!" said the Prince.

Then, "Will you marry me, Erith?"

"It's a queer time to be asking that," replied the goose girl.

"You charged me to ask on my knees," answered the Prince dryly, "and I am here. Will you marry me now?"

"An' it please you," corrected she, with calm blue eyes.

"An' it please you, dear heart," said he, almost meekly. "And we will not be living on your money, for it is all gone."

"Well, I don't mind if I do," answered the goose girl, and cut the ropes.

So they were trothed and kissed one another. And the Prince put her on the front of his own horse and rode with her to the court, where he told the Queen all that had happened and charged her, by her friendship, to get all manner of beautiful raiment and jewels ready and command a great feast that he might marry the goose girl one week from that day, she consenting.

It was the sunniest day ever known in all the world, and the gayest wedding and the fairest bride. And the feasting and dancing lasted for seven days, and there was none in the whole country who went hungry or without a share of the pleasures.

On the seventh day the Prince took his bride back to his own kingdom. They would have no coach, but rode Sable over the hills and pastures and across the common where the geese had once fed, and over the drawbridge and home.

The new Princess had little golden slippers on her feet now, and a robe of rose silk all embroidered with pearls, and a cloak of ermine. But her head was bare, with no crown save that of short golden curls.

TRAMP

Malcolm Carrick

This story takes place in London near St. Paul's Cathedral, just after World War II (1939-1945). Although much of London—including the area around St. Paul's—was heavily bombed during the war, the famous cathedral survived without serious damage.

In the middle of smoky London Town, there was a grassy railway place. There the steam trains, billowing on their way to London Bridge, went under the road. If you leaned over the bridge when one passed, huge clouds of fresh white steam covered you like sheets. When it cleared, you could see St. Paul's. You could walk to St. Paul's from where we lived.

I liked playing in the long grass all by myself. There was a ditch there, and spiky hawthorn bushes grew around the railway signal pole that hummed.

It was better there than in the streets full of other kids' marbles and chalked pavements. Better than listening to the radio where adventures happened to other people, but not to me. Better than the playgrounds on the bomb sites, where gangs of kids picked on me.

In my grassy place, empty like the countryside in books, there was no one to say "Cat got your tongue?"

In my place, *I* made things happen. *I* made the hawthorn into Robin Hood's longbow. *I* made the phantom horse, Black Bess, come alive again. My Black Bess, who did whatever I wanted her to.

When the railway pole hummed loud and pulled its roots from the ground to become a giant stick monster who caught trains and princesses with her spidery lines, I fought her. I whacked her until she went back to being a pole.

Then I'd awaken the Princess with a kiss, like they do in the story and in the pantomime. The Princess was as pretty as Sally James, and she never laughed at my big ears like Sally did.

When Billy the Kid came to London to shoot it out with the Queen, I drew my sword on him. The Queen gave me a medal for that, and a big hug.

No one came to my place then, except the odd animal friend, or the lovers I giggled away.

Every day I played there, but not Sunday. Can't-go-out-to-play day. All of us, big brother Dick, little brother Dave, scratchy in Sunday best. Sitting in the parlor only used on Sunday and Christmas. Everything there smells of polish.

All the family walks to chapel. Outside, Dad talks to Mr. James from across the road. Sally James and her two ugly sisters, all in fluffy white, make faces at me, giggling at my ears sticking out from my new haircut, giggling behind rows of red, grown-up hands clutching Bibles.

Mr. James stares down at me.

Back home at the table, little brother starts singing "Sally, Sally, pride of our alley." Then they all start giggling into their dumplings, trying to make me cry, just because I told Dick I liked Sally. He told every giggling one. Don't cry, do something.

Knock off the plate, SMASH, onto the stone scullery floor. Dumplings dripping, gravy on Uncle's boots, quiet for a moment.

Leave me alone. I know dumplings cost money, I will clean his boots, the plate is only broken in three, Uncle Joe can stick it together again. Uneasy quiet now, Sunday's full of quiet, full of waiting.

At my place the next day, I declared war on everyone who ever stared or giggled at me, made me cry. They all gathered on the other side of the ditch. They grew a hundred times bigger, with long hairy noses, holding plates of gristly meat. "We'll make you eat this!" they jeered.

I shouted for Black Bess and drew my trusty longbow. With my war cry "For England and St. Paul's," I leapt up on Black Bess, together we charged into the ditch—"Oh."

There was someone in the ditch. He moved, dirty, old in a shapeless black coat. He mumbled at me. Tramp.

Run home quick, back to the streets full of uncles and aunts, back to the kitchen full of warm Mum.

"Didn't mean to break the plate, Mum."

"All right, luv, Joe'll fix it."

The next day, Tramp was still there, in *my* place. Dirty thoughts for dirty Tramp. "Go away—" The words shouted in my head but the cat had got my tongue and wouldn't let them out. So I had to send in my Royal troops . . . but they couldn't move him.

Back to the streets where the other kids played, but Black Bess couldn't roam free there.

Back to the radio, where other people had adventures, but not me.

Back to the playgrounds on the bomb sites, where princesses couldn't walk with the rough kids.

Back to my street, where they play ordinary games.

There's Lenny Smith's gang playing soccer. Careful, they're looking at me, they're staring, quick, say something, quick before they see you're scared. . . .

"I . . . I know where there's a tramp."

"Tell us," they said. I told them and they went to see him. I followed them. I saw them throw things at the tramp, sticks and stones, then big things, bricks. But the tramp didn't move.

Then *they* were scared, then Lenny Smith's gang ran away.

Tramp was huddled up quite still. I went close to him. His eyes opened, they looked at me. "It's your fault," his eyes said. Then they closed.

Run home quick, back to the streets full of uncles and aunts, back to the kitchen full of warm Mum, back to the bed full of Brother. But don't tell what happened. Tell-tale-tit, you told Lenny Smith about Tramp.

Come quick, sleep; hurry up, morning. Lamplighter whistling, come on; milkman clinking and clipping over the cobbles in the alley.

Hurry up, Dad's early morning coughing, I must go back to see if Tramp is all right.

But I had to stay in, to wait for the rent-man. It was late before I could get out, back to my place.

Tramp hadn't moved. He was lying in the gathering dew, damp.

"Are you all right?" I asked from a long way away. He didn't answer.

Perhaps he was ill or . . . dead?

I called for Black Bess to ride him to the hospital, but she could only ride in games. There was only me there who could do anything. Only me there to help. I went closer, not breathing. He saw me then. I wanted to run but couldn't. I mustn't. I opened my mouth but no words came out. He touched his lips, he was telling me something. What? What was he telling me?

> Look: Lamps are lit, evening fog is eating St. Paul's.
> Listen: Pianos are jangling in the pubs; wooden wheels,
>   the market stalls are closing.
> Smell: Chips frying. Must be late. Run home quick.

In bed, hissing gaslight makes tramp shadows on the wall. What did tramps put in their mouths? Wine? Beer?

Cigarettes? Medicine? I touched my lips like he did. . . .

"You still hungry?" Dick asks.

"What do tramps eat, Dick?"

"Anything, I suppose."

Hurry up, sleep.

Get into the kitchen early next day, before Mum makes up the fires. Pinch a sandwich from Dad's case, an apple from Brother's schoolbag, a piece of Mum's bread pudding, a bottle of Uncle's beer, all in a paper bag. Off, off to my place, through Waterman Lane Market, get the morning windfall tomatoes, give them a rub, good as new. Off, off to my place.

Tramp was lying still in the ditch. I put the bag near him, then I went right up to him, near the smell, funny smell. Black Bess doesn't smell. I touched him and ran away. I was brave then.

Back home at dinner time, I wasn't brave. Uncle couldn't find his beer. "Who's had it?"

Keep quiet.

We're sent to the pub to get another bottle. Noisy smoky pub, full of legs and jangling piano music.

"You ask, Dick." Dick's brave all the time.

"Mister, get us a bottle of beer for my Uncle Arthur?"

Back at home I jumped every time someone said food. They're all looking a bit sideways at me. Mum's getting the bread pudding out, she'll see . . . THUMP! on the kitchen door. It's Uncle Joe with the mended plate.

"Hello, hello," he laughs.

"Tell us a story, Uncle Joe."

"Tell us a joke, Joe."

Joe tells and talks and laughs while I scoop out some pudding for him so no one notices the hole.

Next day at my quiet grassy place, there were the paper bag and the beer bottle . . . empty. Tramp's eyes were open wide and he looked at me. My tummy had butterflies like when Mum went to get the bread pudding, but I wasn't scared now. Tramp had eaten the food, so he must be better. That made me feel better about telling Lenny Smith.

Tomorrow's Saturday—pocket-money day. Tomorrow I can *buy* food for Tramp, not have to pinch it. "Pay my way," like Dad always says.

Happy, warm in bed, singing downstairs, onions frying, friendly hissing gas. I know what to get Tramp: chips.

Chips. There's two Fish and Chips in our street—Joe's is best. "Fourpennyworth, please. And a pickled onion, please, Mister Joe." Smell the chips wrapped up in newspaper, salted and vinegared. Hot, hot for Tramp.

And medicine, Dad's cough medicine. Run before the chips get cold, back to my place. He's awake. I put the chips in front of him and sat over in the long grass.

"They're hot," I said, proud. He nodded and ate them with dirty fingers, then he half sat up, pointing at the medicine. "That's medicine, if you're ill," I told him. He chuckled into his chips, mumbling at me.

Every day I brought him something to eat. One day I brought a crab's claw from the shellfish man. It cost five pence—chips only cost three pence—but he didn't eat the crab's claw. He liked chips best. He licked the crunchy bits off his beard.

"Were you in the war?" I asked. He had strappings around his feet like soldiers in the army, like Uncle John who wrote letters. He didn't answer. When Mum or Dick didn't answer a question, it meant they were cross or too busy for me or something. But Tramp wasn't cross or busy. So I just talked and it didn't matter if he didn't answer.

All that week and the next, Tramp stayed at my place. Sometimes I'd talk to him, tell him things. If he didn't want to listen, I would play with Black Bess. She didn't mind Tramp being there. Neither did I.

Sometimes I'd make him a person in one of my stories. Usually I made him King of all the Russias, because he had a beard. He just sat and stared and mumbled, and Black Bess and I played around him.

Once on Sunday, I crept out after chapel. I passed Sally James's house. She was at the window and saw me.

"Where are you going?" she asked. "To get your hair cut again?"

"To see my friend," I told her.

"I didn't think you had a friend," she said, not giggling.

"Well, I have." I went on, not feeling shy at all. I was going to *my* place to see *my* friend.

"Tramp, you can be the man in the Bible who got turned into a pillar of salt. Then you don't have to get up." He laughed. "Do you like me?" I asked. He didn't say no.

On Monday I went with chips for Tramp, but he wasn't in the ditch.

"Tramp?" I called out for him, but he wasn't in the grass, he wasn't in the hawthorn, he wasn't anywhere. He had gone.

I just stood, staring at the place where we had been playing only yesterday. After all those chips, after sharing all the things I'd told him, he'd gone without saying.

The chips in my hand got cold and greasy. I flung them over the railway. I hit the railway signal pole, shouted, "I don't care, I don't care, dirty tramp!"

Home. Run home quick, back to the streets full of uncles and aunts, back to the kitchen full of warm Mum, back to the clean washing smell.

"What's the matter?" they asked. Mum, Dad, Uncle, Brothers.

"Nothing," I said. I don't care.

But I did care. I went back to my place later, late, when the warm golden fog was eating St. Paul's, when the evening lamplighter whistled, when the pub piano began to jangle. At my place, I closed my eyes and turned around, hoping he'd be there. He wasn't. I searched the long grass for a message, but I knew I wouldn't find one.

Tramp didn't come back the next day, or the day after . . . he never came back.

He could have been my best friend if he'd wanted. More best than any princess, more best than even Black Bess. No one else had played with us at my place, only Tramp.

He was the only friend I'd ever made by myself; now he had gone. "Why?" I wondered. Perhaps he thought I wasn't a good friend to have, perhaps he thought I was too shy?

"But I'm not shy, am I, Black Bess? And I *was* a good friend to have. I looked after Tramp with chips and stuff. I worried about him. I cared. I bet I'd make someone a good friend."

Wander back slowly home; not so shy.

Back to the streets; not too sad.

Lamps are lit.

It's warm when you remember friends like Tramp.

Warm like the kitchen full of Mum.

Warm like the yellow fog all wrapped around you like a blanket. Sally James came out of the fog. "Your mum's calling for you," Sally said. I smiled. "You'd better go home, Malcolm," Sally said.

"You coming too?" I asked. She didn't answer, but she came. Past the jangling piano pub, with its glowing, colored windows, through the deep yellow blanket we went back to our street.

"Where's your friend?" she asked.

"Gone away," I told her.

"Oh." She put out her hand and touched my arm as gently as a ladybird landing.

At the end of our street, my door was open. We could smell bacon frying through the thick, damp taste of the fog. "Perhaps your supper's ready," smiled Sally.

Someone was singing far away; it was a funny wrapped-up sound. The street was waiting for me and Sally, it looked peaceful . . . safe. Sally's door opened too.

"Sally," I said, "do you like chips?"

ALBERIC THE WISE

Norton Juster

More than many years ago, when fewer things had happened in the world and there was less to know, there lived a young man named Alberic who knew nothing at all. Well, almost nothing, or, depending on your generosity of spirit, hardly anything, for he could hitch an ox and plow a furrow straight or thatch a roof or hone his scythe until the edge was bright and sharp or tell by a sniff of the breeze what the day would bring or with a glance when a grape was sweet and ready. But these were only the things he had to know to live or couldn't help knowing by living and are, as you may have discovered, rarely accounted as knowledge.

Of the world and its problems, however, he knew little, and indeed was even less aware of their existence. In all his life he had been nowhere and seen nothing beyond the remote estate on which he lived and to whose lands he and his family had been bound back beyond the edge of memory. He planted and harvested, threshed and winnowed, tended the hives and the pigs, breathed the country air, and stopped now and again to listen to the birds or puzzle at the wind. There were no mysteries, hopes, or dreams other than those that could be encompassed by his often aching back or impatient stomach. This was the sum of his existence and with it he was neither happy nor sad. He simply could not conceive of anything else.

Since the days were much alike he measured his life by the more discernible seasons—yet they too slipped easily by, and would have continued to do so, I'm sure, had it not been for the lone traveler who appeared unaccountably one chill morning at the close of winter. Alberic watched him make his weary way along the road until, when they stood no more than a glance apart, he paused to rest before continuing on his journey. A curious old man—his tattered tunic was patched-on patches and his worn shoes left hardly a suggestion of leather between himself and the cold ground. He carried a massive bundle on his back and sighed with the pleasure of letting it slide gently from his shoulder to the ground—then just as gently let himself down upon it. He nodded and smiled, mopped his face carefully with a handkerchief easily as old as himself, then acknowledged Alberic's timid greeting and finally began to speak, and when he did it was of many, many things. Where he had come from and where he was bound, what he had seen and what there was yet to discover—commonwealths, kingdoms, empires, counties, and dukedoms—fortresses, bastions, and great solitary castles that dug their fingers into the mountain passes and dared the world to pass— royal courts whose monarchs dressed in pheasant skins and silks and rich brocades of purple and lemon and crimson and bice all interlaced with figures of beasts and blossoms and strange geometric devices—and mountains that had no tops and oceans that had no bottoms.

There seemed no end to what he knew or what he cared to speak about, and speak he did, on and on through the day. His voice was soft and easy but his manner such that even his pauses commanded attention. And as he spoke his eyes sparkled and his words were like maps of unknown lands. He told of caravans that made their way across continents and back with perfumes and oils and dark red wines, sandalwood and lynx hides and ermine and carved sycamore chests, with cloves and cinnamon, precious stones and iron pots and ebony and amber and objects of pure tooled gold—of tall cathedral spires and cities full of life and craft and industry—of ships that sailed in every sea, and of art and science and learned speculation hardly even dreamed of by most people—and of armies and battles and magic and much, much more.

Alberic stood entranced, trying desperately to imagine all these wonderful things, but his mind could wander no further than the fields that he could see, and the images soon would fade or cloud.

"The world is full of wonders," he sighed forlornly, for he realized that he could not even imagine what a wonder was.

"It is everything I've said and even more," the stranger replied, and since it was by now late afternoon he scrambled to his feet and once more took up his heavy bundle. "And remember," he said with a sweep of his arm, "it is all out there, just waiting." Then down the road and across the stubble fields he went.

For weeks after the old man had gone Alberic brooded, for now he knew that there were things he didn't know, and what magic and exciting things they were! Warm wet breezes had begun to blow across the land and the frozen fields had yielded first to mud and then to early blossoms. But now this quiet hillside was not enough to hold his rushing thoughts. "It is all out there, just waiting," he said to himself again and again, repeating the old man's words. When he had repeated them often enough, they became a decision. He secretly packed his few belongings and in the early morning's mist left his home and started down into the world to seek its wonders and its wisdom.

For two days and nights and half another day again he walked—through lonely forests and down along the rushing mountain streams that seemed to know their destination far better than he knew his. Mile after mile he walked until at last the trees and vines gave way to sweeps of easy meadowland and in the distance, barely visible, the towers of a city reflected back the sun's bright rays. As he approached, the hazy form became a jumble of roofs and chimney pots spread out below, and each step closer embellished them with windows, carved gables, domes, and graceful spires. All this in turn was circled by a high wall which seemed to grow higher and wider as he descended towards it, until at last it filled his vision and hid all else behind it. The stream which only days before had been so gay and playful now broadened and, as if aware of its new importance, assumed a slow and dignified pace as it passed through the city. Alberic paused for a moment to catch his breath, then, with a slight shiver of anticipation, passed beneath the cool dark gates and entered the city too.

What a teeming, busy place! Houses and shops, music and movement, all kinds of noises, signs, and smells, and more people than he ever knew existed. He wandered along the cobbled streets delighted by each new discovery and noting with care the strange new sights and sounds so unfamiliar to his country senses. He soon learned too that he had come to a city famous above all others for the beautiful stained glass manufactured in its workshops.

"A noble and important profession," he decided soberly, "for surely beauty is the true aim of wisdom!" Without delay he went off to apprentice himself to the greatest of the master glassmakers.

"Well, well," growled the old craftsman after examining Alberic carefully, "so you want to make glass. Very well, we shall see. Your duties will be few and simple. Each morning you'll arise before the birds and with the other apprentices fetch sixty barrows of firewood from the forest. Then in each furnace bank a fire precisely hot enough to melt the lead and fuse the glass, and keep them tended constantly so that none goes out or varies even slightly in its heat. Then, of course, work the bellows, fetch the ingots from the foundry, run errands, assist the journeymen as they need, sharpen and repair all the chisels, files, knives, scrapers, shears, mallets, and grozing irons so that each is in perfect order, make deliveries quickly and courteously, grind and mix the pigments, work the forge, sweep out the shop, fetch, carry, stoop, haul, and bend, and in your spare time help with the household chores. You can of course eat your fill of the table scraps and sleep on the nice warm floor. Well, don't just stand there, you've only started and you're already hours behind in your work." When he finished he smiled a benevolent smile, for he was known for his generous nature.

Alberic applied himself to his new tasks with diligence, working from early morning until late at night, when he would curl up in one corner of the shop to dream happily of the day's accomplishments and carefully sort and pack into his memory everything he'd learned. For some time he did only the menial jobs, but soon under the watchful eye of the master he began taking part in more important and exacting procedures. He learned to chip and shape the glass into pieces often no larger than the palm of his hand and then apply the colors mixed in gum or oil with a delicate badger brush and fire these to permanence in the glowing kilns. Then from measurements and patterns he learned to set each piece in the grooved strips of lead and solder them carefully at each joint. For almost two years he worked and watched as all these small and painstaking operations took form in great windows and medallions of saintly lives or tales of moral instruction which glowed in deep splendid blues and vivid rubies.

Finally the time came for Alberic to prove his skill and take his place among the glassmakers—to create a work entirely on his own. He was determined that it would be a rare and lovely thing and he set about it with quiet intensity.

"What will it be, Alberic?" they all asked eagerly.

"Beautiful," he replied with never a moment's doubt, and that was all he'd say.

And for weeks he worked secretly in one corner of the shop until the day came when his work was to be judged. Everyone gathered to see it. The master looked long and carefully. He stood back to view it in the light and squinted close at matters of fine detail, and then he rubbed his chin and then he tapped his finger and then he swayed and then he sighed and then he frowned.

"No," he said sadly and slowly, "certainly not. You will never be a glassmaker." And everyone agreed, for despite the best of intentions Alberic's work was poor indeed.

How miserable he was! How thoroughly miserable! Why wasn't it beautiful when he had tried so hard? How could he have learned so much and yet still fail? No one knew the answer. "There is no reason now for me to stay," he said quietly, gathering up his bundle, and without even as much as a last look back he walked out into the lonely countryside. For several days he wandered aimlessly, seeing nothing, heading nowhere, his thoughts turned inward to his unhappy failure.

But it was spring, and no one who has ever worked the land can long ignore the signs this season brings. Sweet promising smells hung gently in the warm air, and all around the oxlips, daisies, and celandine splashed the fields in lively yellow. A graceful bird and then another caught Alberic's eye. The busy buzz and click of smaller things were reassuring to his ear and even the bullfrogs' heavy thump set his heart beating once again. His spirits and then his hope revived. The world seemed large and inviting once again.

"There are other places and other things to learn," he thought. "Beauty isn't everything. The true measure of wisdom is utility. I'll do something useful." He hurried now and before long came to a city whose stonecutters and masons were renowned throughout the world for the excellence of their work. His thoughts turned to castles and cloisters, massive walls, towering vaults, and steeples which only miracles of skill could hold suspended in the air.

"Everything of use and value is made of stone," he concluded and rushed to seek employment with the master stonecutter.

And for two more years he busied himself learning the secrets of this new vocation—selecting and cutting only the finest stone from the quarry—matching, marking, and extracting the giant blocks to be moved on heavy wheeled carts to each new building—and then noting carefully how each shaped stone was fitted in its place so that walls and buttresses grew and arches sprang from pier to pier with such precision that no blade, however sharp, could slip between the joints. Soon he learned to mix and measure mortar and operate the windlasses whose ingenious ropes and pulleys allowed one man to lift for fifty. Then to make his first careful cuts with bolster and chisel and then stop and watch again as surer hands than his cut and shaped the graceful moldings and intricate tracery which brought the stone to life. As he worked, he questioned and remembered everything he saw and heard, and as each day passed, his confidence and his knowledge grew and he began to think of his future life as a great and skillful stonecutter.

When the time came for him to prove his skill to the masons and sculptors of the guild, Alberic chose a piece of specially fine, delicately veined marble and set to work. It was to be the finest carving they had ever seen. With great care he studied and restudied the block and planned his form, then cut into the stone in search of it. He worked in a fever of excitement, his sharp chisels biting off the unwanted material in large chips and pieces. But the image he saw so clearly in his mind seemed always to be just out of sight, a little deeper in the stone. The block grew smaller and the mound of dust and chips larger, and still, like a phantom, the form seemed to recede and still he chased it. Soon there was nothing left at all. The great block of stone had disappeared and, soon afterwards, the stonecutter too. For again, without a word, Alberic gathered up his belongings and passed through the city gate. He had failed once more.

"Usefulness isn't everything," he decided after roaming about disconsolately for several days. "Innovation is surely a measure of wisdom. I'll do something original."

The opportunity presented itself in the very next town, where the goldsmiths, it was said, produced objects of unsurpassed excellence and fancy. Bowls and magic boxes, mirrors, shields and scepters, crowns, rings, enchanted buckles and clasps, and candlesticks and vases of incredible grace and intricacy spilled from these workshops and found their way to every royal court and market in the land. It was here that Alberic learned to draw and shape the fine gold wire and work the thin sheets of metal into patterns and textures of light and shape and then inlay these with delicate enamels and precious stones. It was here also that he worked and hoped for the next two years of his life and it was here that for the third time he failed and for the third time took his disappointment to the lonely countryside.

And so it went, from town to town, from city to city, each noted for its own particular craft or enterprise. There were potters who turned and shaped their wet clay into graceful bowls and tall jugs fire-glazed with brilliant cobalt, manganese, and copper oxides. Leather finishers who transformed smooth soft skins into shoes and boots, gloves, tunics, bombards, bottles, and buckets. There were weavers and spinners who worked in wools and silks, carpenters and cabinetmakers, glassblowers, armorers, and tinkers. There were scholars who spent their days searching out the secrets of ancient books, and chemists and physicians, and astronomers determining the precise distances between places that no one had ever seen. And busy ports which offered men the sea and all it touched, and smiths and scribes and makers of fine musical instruments, for anyone with such a bent. Alberic tried them all—and watched and learned and practiced and failed and then moved on again. Yet he kept searching and searching for the one thing that he could do—the secret of the wisdom and skill he so desired.

The years passed and still he traveled on—along the roads and trails and half-forgotten paths—across plains and deserts and forests whose tangled growth held terrors that were sometimes real and sometimes even worse— over hills and cruel high mountain passes and down again perhaps along some unnamed sea—until at last, alone and old and tired, he reached the ramparts of the great capital city.

"I will never find wisdom," he sighed. "I'm a failure at everything."

At the edge of the market square Alberic set his bundle down and watched longingly as all the students, artisans, and craftsmen went unconcernedly about their business. He wiped the dust from his eyes and sat for a moment, thinking of his future and his past. What a strange sight he was! His beard was now quite long and gray and the cloak and hat and shoes bore evidence of some repair from every place he'd been. His great bundle bulged with the debris of a lifetime's memories and disappointments and his face was a sad scramble of much the same. As he rummaged through his thoughts, a group of children, struck by his uncommon look, stopped and gathered close around him.

"Where have you come from?"

"What do you do?"

"Tell us what you've seen," they eagerly asked, and poised to listen or flee as his response required.

Alberic was puzzled. What could he tell them? No one had ever sought his conversation before, or asked his opinion on any question. He scratched his head and rubbed his knees, then slowly and hesitantly began to speak, and suddenly the sum of all those experiences, which lay packed up in his mind as in some disordered cupboard, came back to him. He told them of a place or two he'd been and of some lands they'd never known existed and creatures that all their wildest fancies could not invent, and then a story, a legend, and three dark mysterious tales remembered from a thousand years before. As he spoke, the words began to come more easily and the pleasure of them eased away his weariness. Everything he'd ever seen or heard or touched or tried was suddenly fresh and clear in his memory, and when the children finally left for home, their faces glowing with excitement, it was to spread the news of the wonderful old man who knew so much.

Since he had no place else to go, Alberic returned to the square each day, and each day the crowds grew larger and larger around him. At first it was only the children, but soon everyone, regardless of age or size, crowded close to listen—and patiently he tried to tell them all they wished to hear. For many of their questions his own experience provided the answers, and for those he could not directly answer he always had a tale or story whose point or artifice led them to answers of their own. More and more he began to enjoy the days, and soon he learned to embellish his tales with skillful detail, to pause at just the right time, to raise his voice to a roar or lower it to a whisper as the telling demanded. And the crowds grew even larger.

Workmen came to listen and stayed to learn the secret ways and methods of their own crafts. Artisans consulted him on questions of taste or skill and when they left they always knew more than when they came. Alberic told them everything he had learned or seen through all his failures and his wanderings and before very long he became known throughout the realm as Alberic the Wise. His fame spread so far that one day the King himself and several of his ministers came to the square to see for themselves. Cleverly disguised so as not to alert the old man to his purpose, the King posed several questions concerning matters of state and situations in far-off corners of the kingdom. Everything he asked, Alberic answered in great detail, enlarging each reply with accounts of the lore and customs of each region, condition of the crops and royal castles, local problems and controversies, reports on the annual rainfall, and the latest depredations by various discontented barons. And for added measure, two songs and a short play (in which he acted all the parts) which he had learned before being dismissed from a traveling theater company.

"You are the wisest man in my kingdom," the astonished King proclaimed, throwing off his disguise, "and you shall have a palace of your own with servants and riches as befits a man of your accomplishments."

Alberic moved into the new palace at once and was more than content with his new life. He enjoyed the wealth and possessions he had never known before, slept on feather beds, ate nothing but the most succulent and delicate foods, and endlessly put on and took off the many cloaks, robes, and caps the King had graciously provided. His beard was trimmed and curled and he spent his time strolling about the gardens and marble halls posing with proper dignity before each mirror and repeating to himself in various tones and accents, "Alberic the Wise, ALBERIC THE WISE, A-L-B-E-R-I-C T-H-E W-I-S-E!" in order to become accustomed to his new title.

After several weeks, however, the novelty began to wear thin, for a sable cloak is just a sable cloak and a *poulet poêle à l'estragon* is really just another roast chicken. Soon doubts began to crowd out pleasures, and by degrees he grew first serious, then sober, then somber, and then once again thoroughly discouraged.

"How is it possible to be a failure at everything one day and a wise man the next?" he inquired. "Am I not the same person?"

For weeks this question continued to trouble him deeply, and since he could not find a satisfactory answer he returned to the square with his doubts.

"Simply calling someone wise does not make him wise!" he announced to the eager crowd. "So you see, I am not wise." Then, feeling much better, he returned to the palace and began to make ready to leave.

"How modest," the crowd murmured. "The sign of a truly great man." And a delegation of prominent citizens was sent to prevail on him to stay.

Even after listening to their arguments, Alberic continued to be troubled, and the very next day he returned to the square again.

"Miscellaneous collections of fact and information are not wisdom," he declared fervently. "Therefore I am not wise!" And he returned and ordered workmen to begin boarding up the palace.

"Only the wisest of men would understand this," the people all agreed, and petitions were circulated to prevent his leaving.

For several more days he paced the palace corridors unhappily and then returned for a third time.

"A wise man's words are rarely questioned," he counseled gently. "Therefore you must be very careful whom you call wise."

The crowd was so grateful for his timely warning that they cheered for fully fifteen minutes after he had returned to the palace.

Finally, in desperation, he reappeared that very afternoon and stated simply, "For all the years of my life I have sought wisdom and to this day I still do not know even the meaning of the word, or where to find it," and, thinking that would convince them, he ordered a carriage for six o'clock that afternoon.

The crowd gasped. "No one but a man of the most profound wisdom would ever dare to admit such a thing," they all agreed, and an epic poem was commissioned in his honor.

Once again Alberic returned to the palace. The carriage was canceled, the rooms were opened and aired. There was nothing he could say or do to convince them that he wasn't what they all thought him to be. Soon he refused to answer any more questions or, in fact, to speak at all, and everyone agreed that because of the troubled times this was certainly the wisest thing to do. Each day he grew more morose and miserable, and though his fame continued to grow and spread he found no more satisfaction in his success than he had in all his failures. He slept little and ate less and his magnificent robes began to hang like shrouds. The bright optimism that had shone in his eyes through all his travels and hardships began to fade, and as the months passed he took to spending all his time at the top of the great north tower, staring without any interest at nothing in particular.

"I am no wiser now than I was before," he said one afternoon, thinking back across the years. "For I still don't know what I am or what I'm looking for." But as he sat there remembering and regretting, he sensed in the air the barest suggestion of some subtle yet familiar scent that drifted in on the freshening breeze. What it was he didn't know—perhaps the pungent tangled aroma of some far eastern bazaar or the sharp and honest smell of a once-known workshop, or it might have been simply the sweet clean air of an upland field, the memory of which had long been lost in detail yet retained in some more durable way; but whatever it was, it grew stronger and stronger, stirring something deep within him and taking hold of all his thoughts and feelings. His spirit suddenly quickened in response and each breath now came faster than the one before. And then for just a moment he sat quite still—and then at last he knew.

"I am not a glassmaker nor a stonecutter, nor a goldsmith, potter, weaver, tinker, scribe, or chef," he shouted happily, and he leaped up and bounded down the steep stone stairs. "Nor a vintner, carpenter, physician, armorer, astronomer, baker, or boatman." Down and around he ran as fast as he could go along the palace corridors until he reached the room in which all his old things had been stored. "Nor a blacksmith, merchant, musician, or cabinetmaker," he continued as he put on the ragged cloak and shoes and hat. "Nor a wise man or a fool, success or failure, for no one but myself can tell me what I am or what I'm not."

And when he'd finished he looked into the mirror and smiled and wondered why it had taken him so long to discover such a simple thing.

So Alberic picked up his bundle, took one last look through the palace, and went down to the square for the last time.

"I have at last discovered one thing," he stated simply. "It is much better to look for what I may never find than to find what I do not really want." And with that he said goodbye and left the city as quietly as he'd come.

The crowd gasped and shook their heads in disbelief.

"He has given up his palace!"

"And his wealth and servants!"

"And the King's favor!"

"And he does not even know where he is going," they buzzed and mumbled. "How foolish, how very foolish! How could we ever have thought him wise?" And they all went home.

But Alberic didn't care at all, for now his thoughts were full of all the things he had yet to see and do and all the times he would stop to tell his stories and then move on again. Soon the walls were far behind and only his footsteps and the night were there to keep him company. Once again he felt the freedom and the joy of not knowing where each new step would take him, and as he walked along his stride was longer and stronger than was right somehow for a man his age.

PODHU AND ARUWA

African folktale
as told by Humphrey Harman

Old Ramogi lived with all his family by the shores of the Great Lake. And what a family! There was Ramogi's wife, and his seven sons: Onyango and Ouma and Agwanda and Obwavo and Oyako and Podhu and Aruwa. Then *all* the sons were married and so there were seven wives and a swarm of small brown naked children *and* half a dozen poor relations and . . . and . . . and . . . More like a village than a family. Dozens of solid little houses with mud walls and yellow thatch and round them all a big hedge of ojuok and, outside that, gardens full of maize and millet and beans, and herds of cattle grazing in the water meadows, and bands of young men hunting deer and pig in the reeds.

Of course with so many people living on top of one another one could expect arguments and rows and so indeed there were, little ones all the time but sometimes big ones when everybody shouted for hours. Then, when a pot had been broken and someone had lost his temper properly and reached for a spear, Ramogi would bellow from the house where he was resting and that would be that and everyone would be quiet until the next time. He was the head of the family and you did as you were told or you could go and carve yourself a field out of the Great Forest and live by yourself.

No one wanted to do that.

The Great Forest began a mile away to the east, very dark, very secret, full of strange sounds at night. It was a threatening place and mixed up with magic of the worst kind. The Elephant Folk lived there and the family of Ramogi left it strictly alone, for no one wishes to be turned into a tree or an ape or wander forever lost in a place where the sunlight is strained through so many leaves that it hardly reaches the ground.

On the other side of the village was a hill that was covered with rocks. But this was a cheerful place and was called Ramogi; and whether the hill was named after the man or the man after the hill no one was quite sure, and indeed the matter was one for much argument on hot afternoons in the shade of a tree when the crops were in and nobody had much to do. Ramogi could have cleared the matter up perhaps, but he preferred to leave it alone, believing that it kept everyone harmlessly occupied and out of mischief.

Well, Ramogi had lived a good life but in the end he grew old and died, and Onyango, the eldest son, took his place and then it was time for all the other brothers to move on and make villages of their own. For although one usually listens to a father when he tells you to behave, no one takes much notice of a brother. And so they moved, going west along the lake or north into the plain, but not east, for that was toward the Great Forest. You couldn't go south unless you had webbed feet and anyone who has listened properly can understand why.

All the brothers went singly with their wives and children and followers and all of them settled on good land and built strong houses and did well and since five of them don't come into this story again, we needn't bother about them anymore.

Except for Podhu and Aruwa, the youngest. They loved each other so dearly that each was unhappy if he did not know where the other was. Always they had been together. As little boys they had watched Ramogi's cows in the pasture and made their own toy cows out of wet clay from the ant heaps. At night they curled asleep on the same skin and when they were bigger they hunted together. They had married sisters. Always they did the same things and thought the same thoughts and sometimes one would start a sentence and stop and the other would finish it without hesitation. Generally people considered them as one person, which was sometimes awkward for their wives, because if you borrowed something from one brother's house and returned it to the other it could lead to misunderstanding.

And so when all their brothers had gone, except Onyango, who was asking pointed questions about when they expected to move, Podhu looked at Aruwa and Aruwa looked at Podhu and then Podhu said:

"Brother, it is time we also were going to look for land of our own."

Aruwa was busy covering the two mouths of a small drum with well-scraped skin and had got to the ticklish bit where you lace the skin tightly and although you hold the drum with your feet and one hand and pull one thong with the other and another with your teeth, you could really do with two more hands. So he took a long time answering and it came out in jerks.

"Mm . . . yes . . . (mumble, mumble) . . . hold this thong a moment, Brother . . . yes, indeed . . . which direction . . . bother the thing! . . . ah, that's better . . . which direction did *you* think of going, Brother?"

"Well," said Podhu, "it's a mite difficult."

He began ticking off names on his fingers.

"Agwanda and Ouma have gone along the lake shore and so *they* won't want anyone else there. And Obwavo and Oyako have gone north and anyway, I never did think much of that plains country. I thought of going east."

"Into the forest, Brother?"

"*Beside* the forest, Aruwa. There's good land there running right down to the lake and plenty of wood at hand for the houses."

Aruwa finished knotting the thongs, put the drum between his knees, and tapped a little tune. He was a good musician.

"You know, Podhu," he said, shutting his eyes to listen to his own music, "I had something of the same idea. But is there room for two?"

Podhu considered.

"Not for two farms. Hardly enough for that. There would be enough for one big farm if we lived together."

Aruwa opened his eyes and looked at the sky and said to no one in particular:

"There is a saying among our people that although even cats and dogs can live peaceably together, brothers never can."

"I know," said Podhu, "but I thought we might try."

"An excellent idea," replied Aruwa. "We'll go east, to the Great Forest."

And so, very shortly afterward, they did, and built their house just where the forest became thin and gave up and turned to grass, and everything went so well with them that "to agree like Podhu and Aruwa" began to be a saying in that part of the world.

All might have gone on well if it hadn't been for Aruwa's magic spear.

Before Ramogi died he gave one thing of his possessions to each of his sons. Onyango got his feathered headdress, Ouma his fly-whisk made from a cow's tail. Aruwa had been given a spear.

Ramogi had had many spears and this was not the one he used for hunting before he grew too stiff in the legs, or any of the half a dozen that lay across the rafters of his house and were borrowed by the boys when they became old enough to use them. This was an old, old spear that had belonged to Ramogi's father and his father before that and had been made by the smiths of a people called the Nandi who were skilled in all kinds of ironwork. It had a long narrow blade shaped like a reed and Ramogi had treasured it and never permitted any of his sons to touch it. When they had asked why, he had always told them it was a magic spear and they had believed him. It became Aruwa's most treasured possession and leaned against the center post in the new house that he shared with Podhu.

One morning, when they had lived in their new house for a year and the season was at its height and the maize stood straight and stiff in the fields like soldiers, the tassels wet with dew, Aruwa drove the cattle out and Podhu stayed home and slept late.

He was awakened by cries from the women and behind all this noise a splashy sound of green maize stalks being crushed.

He sat for a moment, muddled with sleep, and then he made out words from the cries.

"Elephants! The Elephant Folk are in the maize!"

Podhu jumped up and seized a spear (it was Aruwa's precious one), ran out of the house, through the gateway in a moment, leapt a thorn hedge into the maize, and then stopped suddenly. The field seemed full of elephants. With their great backs shiny black with dew and wide ears spread, they forged through the maize like ships and the wet stalks smashed beneath them. Dozens of elephants, each spoiling more than a man could eat in a year, tearing

146

it up by sheaves with their wicked, snaky trunks and stuffing it into their mouths.

Podhu lost his temper and became reckless. He ran through the maize until he reached the edge of the desert of smashed plants, burst into the open, and gave a great yell of rage. There was a sudden silence. Every elephant stood stock-still and their great heads turned and regarded Podhu with grave amazement.

Then he flung Aruwa's spear with all his strength at the biggest elephant. He saw it stick in a wrinkled side and at that all the herd turned, screaming with anger and panic, stamped flat a hedge in their way, and crashed off into the forest . . . and on, on . . . the noise fading . . . until at last it vanished.

And with it Aruwa's spear.

As a matter of fact, when the elephants were out of sight of Podhu they stopped, pulled themselves together, and were more than a little ashamed. They took the spear out of the old bull, who grumbled dreadfully but was not much hurt, and then they took it back to the great clearing, deep in the forest, which was their home and which no one had ever found. There they stored the spear carefully with the other things they had picked up in their wanderings. Elephants are wasteful only about people's crops; they can be very economical about other things.

When Aruwa came home with the cattle, tired and hungry, his wife told him about the spear. He was furious. His precious spear gone off, stuck in the hide of an elephant! Were there not a dozen other spears of no

147

particular value to throw at elephants if that was what Podhu wanted to do?

Podhu said that he was sorry.

Aruwa muttered under his breath and went to the edge of the forest to see if the spear had been knocked out against a tree. There was no spear and the sight of the ruined maize didn't improve his temper.

Podhu, who was very hurt, offered to buy him the best spear that could be made in the country.

Aruwa shouted: "I want my father's magic spear and only that. I'll not forget it if you give me the whole world. And if you don't bring it back I will kill you!"

"Very well," said Podhu, "I will get it or die in the attempt."

"You'll get it," sneered Aruwa. "And how? I suppose you will go and ask the elephants for it back?"

"Yes," said Podhu. "I will do exactly that."

That night everyone went to bed in the kind of sulky silence that follows a big family row.

The very next morning, before anyone else was awake, Podhu took a spear, slung a skin bag over one shoulder, and leaving the house, walked to the forest. At its edge he took one last look at the morning sun rising over the lake shore and then he grasped his spear firmly and pushed his way in among the trees.

There all was cold and green and gloomy, like a fish's world at the bottom of a pond. He found paths made by wild pigs and timid deer, and these he followed, his feet silent on the wet leaves. All that day he walked, going deeper and deeper until he knew he was where no man had been before, but still he found no sign of the Elephant Folk.

At last it grew even darker, and although he could not see it, he knew that the sun was setting. He found a tree whose great roots writhed from halfway up its trunk and fell in gigantic careless coils on the forest floor and, crawling in amongst these, he discovered a hollow full of dry leaves. In this he sat and ate his cold maize cake and then tried to sleep. Light vanished and the forest, so silent all day, grew full of noises: rustlings and croaking sounds, the hooting of owls, once a mysterious scream from high above his head and another time the heavy trampling of something big. Podhu trembled with cold and fear and at any moment expected to find himself changed into something unpleasant.

At last he slept and when he awoke it was as light as it ever got in that forest, and he stretched and finished his food and went on his way. Many hours later he came to a track which, it seemed to him, had not been made by an animal. He followed it slowly to a small clearing in the trees and there he found a tumble-down hut with the smoke of a cooking fire streaming through its thatch. As he watched this, uncertain what to do, an old bent Dorobo woman came through the doorway carrying a chopper and began to cut herself some wood from the dead boughs that lay about the clearing. As she worked she grumbled to herself.

"Eh! Eh! What it is to be old and have no grandson to cut wood for his grannie!"

Podhu listened to this, and more, for a while, and then, finding nothing dangerous here, he stepped into the clearing. The old woman gave a little scream of fright and surprise.

"I'll cut the wood, Mother," said Podhu, and he took the chopper from her hand, laid aside his spear, and set about it. In ten minutes he had a fine pile, and taking an armful, he carried it to the door of the hut.

"May I enter your house, Mother?" he asked, for among Podhu's people, as among others, one does not walk into strange houses without asking.

The old woman had got over her fright and had seated herself upon a log to watch him work. Now she gave a cackle of laughter.

"Eh!" she babbled. "A fine young man. The first I've seen for many a long year. And what are you doing here, all alone so far from your friends, eh? Asking to go into my house! How do you know I'm not a witch, young man? How do you know that once you're in my house I shan't turn you into an ape, or a snake, or a little crawling lizard, eh?"

"Mother," said Podhu, "I'm tired and I'm lost. I don't think you're a witch, for I listened to you before you saw me and if you had been one I think you would have known I was there. You only sounded like an old woman who needed the help of a strong grandson. I'll tell you why I'm here, but first let me go in and put down this wood and sit by the fire, for I've not seen one for two days."

Then they went into the house and mended the fire and the old woman shared her meal with Podhu and afterward he told her his story. She listened, nodding her head at the important places, and when he had done she said:

"Ah, but you're a bold young man to come to such a dangerous place as this on such an errand. Perhaps I will help you and perhaps I won't. Perhaps I *can* help you and perhaps I can't. We'll see. Meanwhile let's find out what sort of a grandson you make. You stop here and chop the wood until I make up my mind."

So Podhu lived with the old Dorobo woman, and what a time she gave him! Up in the morning at the crack of dawn, fetching water from the stream, gathering roots, hoeing her little patch of vegetables, chopping wood. That little fire of hers burned more wood than a family of charcoal burners. He chopped wood every minute of the day that he was not doing the other tasks she demanded. And all day long her scolding banged about his ears.

"Eh! What a grandson! Lazy, worthless, idle, graceless! Fit for nothing but polishing the seat of a stool! Podhu! Wood! You haven't brought the wood and the fire's almost out. Eh!"

Every evening he asked her: "Mother, are you going to help me get Aruwa's spear?" and she answered: "What? What's that he says? Spear? Ah, we'll see about that. We'll see."

When he had worked a month for her and was in despair, suddenly, one afternoon, she smiled and told him to stop what he was doing and come and sit beside her.

"Now listen, my son," she said. "Perhaps you think that you've wasted your time here, but that's not true. We Dorobo know the Elephant Folk and we know that a man must have three things if he is to succeed with them. He must have courage and that you have or you would not be here. He must have also patience and goodness, and that I had to find out. Even with these it will be dangerous to speak with them, for you have injured one and they do not easily forget that. But I'll give you something that may help a little and after that you must just trust to your luck."

Then from underneath the skin she wore the old Dorobo woman took a small blue bead as big as a bean. It glowed like a piece of sky and when she placed it on Podhu's open hand he could see into it but not through it.

"That, my son, is a magic bead. Our hunters carry it when they hunt the elephant, and if they are good and patient and brave then *sometimes* the elephants do what they wish them to. Tomorrow I will show you the path that leads to the kraal of the Elephant Folk and you must take your chance or go home without your brother's spear."

Early next morning the old Dorobo woman took Podhu to a small track that left the clearing. "Follow this," she said. "Where it divides, take the bigger; where it becomes three, take the middle one. In perhaps four hours you will come to the kraal of the Elephant Folk. Leave your spear and everything that you carry or wear except the bead and go round the kraal wall until you find the entrance. Then enter boldly and stand where they can see you, with your eyes to the ground. Don't speak until you are spoken to and then, if they don't kill you first, you must speak up boldly and ask for what you want."

Then Podhu thanked her and followed the track. And where it divided he took the bigger and where it spread into three he took the middle. He went as silently as he was able and the trees about him seemed to get bigger and older and more twisted until suddenly, after four hours, the path stopped at the foot of an immense wall of uprooted trees piled and flung higgledy-piggledy one on top of the other.

This must be the hedge of the elephants' kraal, he thought, and looking to right and left he saw that this wall of branches and trunks and creepers curved away through the trees on either side. Podhu turned along a small path that followed the hedge until he saw before him a wide road beaten out of the forest by many huge feet. He saw that this road ran through a gap in the kraal wall and he judged that this was the entrance. Then, remembering the old Dorobo woman's advice, he laid his spear and skin bag and the skin he wore and the necklace round his neck all on the ground; and, taking only the blue bead, he stepped naked into the road,

153

and with his heart thumping in his chest he walked slowly through the entrance.

Before him was a vast expanse of beaten earth many times greater than the biggest field Podhu had ever seen. There seemed to be only the entrance he had come through, for the great hedge curled right round him and the trees outside this hung over, their branches giving shade. In this were hundreds and hundreds of elephants, more than Podhu had imagined to be in the whole world. All kinds of elephants, old and young, great bulls with polished white tusks, wrinkled cows fussing over calves which stood between their legs. All about him ears flapped, heads tossed, tails twisted, and black trunks swung. One great fig tree stood within the hedge on the far side of the kraal and beneath this rested a gigantic old bull as big as a hill, so old that his skin hung in folds, his tusks so heavy that his head hung down with the weight of them. This Podhu judged to be the chief, and marking his position, Podhu bent his head and walked unsteadily toward him, panting through dry lips.

When first he had entered there had come a silence over the elephants, then all about him Podhu heard them stirring like rocks rumbling down a hillside. The deep grumbling in a thousand throats turned to a roar of anger and a young bull screamed: "Kill him! It's the man who threw the spear."

By the time that Podhu stopped in front of the chief (he could only see his feet for he kept his head bent) he knew, although no one had touched him, that they were all pressing close and he could feel the ground trembling as they rolled forward. Or perhaps it was his own trembling. He stood still waiting to be killed and then the noise about him grew less and at last there was nothing except for a monstrous breathing.

It seemed to Podhu that he stood like this for a long time, a small, naked, shivering Podhu. Then he heard a thin tired voice that somehow *sounded* gray. It was the old chief and he might have been speaking to himself.

"A man," he said gently. "An animal who walks more upright than an ape, looking like a forked stick. A creature without mercy or pity. Of all living things why have *you* come here?"

Podhu was so surprised that he forgot to be afraid. He had never thought of himself as being like that. He looked up at the old bull and spoke up boldly so that all could hear.

"Elephant Folk, when you came to graze in my garden I was unkind to you. I took my brother's spear and threw it and by ill luck it struck one of you who took it with him back to the forest. My brother now says that I must give him back his spear or he will kill me. That is why I have come here. Either give me back my spear or kill me as I deserve."

When he had finished his speech there was a long silence and then all the elephants began to talk at once until they realized that their chief was speaking. Then immediately they were quiet.

"... my brothers ..." he was saying. "We must not behave like this or our visitor here will mistake us for men."

The elephants shuffled their feet on the beaten mud (they rasped like giant files on wood), and grumbled.

"My friend," said the old bull to Podhu, "I think that you had better leave us for a little while so that we may decide what shall be done with you."

Then two elephants led Podhu away across the kraal and allowed him to sit in the shade while the rest called a meeting. The discussion was long and excited. Podhu could hear one or more of them trumpeting from where he sat with his two guards, but at last all grew still and he realized that they had made up their minds about him. He was led back to the council and the old bull spoke again.

"Young man," he said, "if we have your brother's spear we will give it to you because you are brave and because we like your impudence in coming here. But first you must promise us two things."

Podhu, whose heart had begun to sing with relief, became serious again.

"First you must teach your sons to build little huts beside your growing maize. And in those huts, in each field, a child shall sit and watch. Then when we Elephant Folk come to eat, the child shall run out and bang an iron pot and when we hear that we shall go away and leave the crop alone. How else can we tell what is yours by planting and what is ours since it grows by nature?"

"That I'll do," said Podhu (and so he did, for always now in Africa a child watches the ripening maize and the animals will usually respect the clatter of his beaten pot).

"Next," went on the chief, "you must promise not to tell anyone the way to this place."

"That I'll do willingly," said Podhu (and no one has ever again found the elephants' kraal, as they would have done if Podhu had broken his promise).

Then they led him round behind the fig tree, and there, stacked in rows, were hundreds of spears that had been brought by the elephants and, among them, Podhu's eager eye at once saw Old Ramogi's magic spear. He took it, and bowing low to the old bull, he thanked them all for their kindness and went away.

He collected the things he had left beside the kraal hedge and began his journey home. He meant to thank the old Dorobo woman who had helped him but he could never again find the clearing where she lived and sometimes he wondered if she *had* been a witch after all, for not all witches are wicked. But indeed on that journey he became so thoroughly lost that he wandered for three days before he found his way out of the forest and back to his home.

There all his people came running to meet him and he waved Aruwa's spear on high and Aruwa took it with shining eyes, he was so happy to get it back. He was in fact so pleased that he forgot to thank Podhu.

Then everyone asked questions and Podhu told his story (he was, of course, careful to say nothing that would betray the elephants' kraal) and when he reached the end he took out the blue bead and showed it to them all.

Everyone gasped at its beauty. It glowed more wonderfully than ever in that sunny place and it passed from hand to hand with exclamations of admiration and wonder. Down the line of women it went, who handled it enviously and parted with it slowly, until it reached the children. They hardly dared touch such a magic thing and passed it on quickly until it reached the hands of Aruwa's smallest son, whose name was Onyango. And Onyango, who was not old enough to know better, popped it into his mouth and swallowed it.

Consternation!

When they realized what had happened you never heard such a row. Everyone shouted advice. Podhu's wife (who fancied wearing that bead) screamed and picked up little Onyango by the heels and thumped him on the back. Onyango yelled. Aruwa's wife thought her son was being killed and attacked her sister (the brothers had married sisters, you will remember) and pulled her hair. Three cooking pots were broken and an old servant of Aruwa's fell in the fire and had to be sat in the stream to put him out. He wasn't hurt and no one was very sorry for him because he was always doing it to attract attention.

But the bead was inside little Onyango and there it stayed.

Then Podhu, who was gray with anger, said to Aruwa: "My brother, when I lost your magic spear you said that

I must get it back or you would kill me. Then when I risked my life with the elephants and did get it back you failed to thank me. Now, Brother, I think that the stick is about another back. Your son has swallowed my magic bead. What are you going to do about it?"

Aruwa answered: "Brother, before we came here I mentioned the saying of our people that it is easier for cats and dogs to live together without quarreling than it is for brothers. We have between us showed that to be a true saying. Tomorrow I will move to another place and make my village alone, like the rest of our brothers."

"I think that will be best," said Podhu, "but Onyango, your son, must stay with me as my son, for he has my magic bead."

Then Aruwa bowed his head, for he loved his son but admitted the justice of what Podhu said.

And so it was done and afterward the brothers lived apart and there were no more quarrels. As for Onyango, he stayed with his new father, Podhu, and didn't mind a bit after the first few days, for Podhu loved him also. But he got a new name, for always afterward he was known as Onyango Who Has the Bead.

And so far as I know he has it still.

THE INVISIBLE CHILD

Tove Jansson

One dark and rainy evening the
Moomin family sat around the
veranda table picking over
the day's mushroom harvest.
The big table was covered with newspapers, and in the
center of it stood the lighted kerosene lamp. But the
corners of the veranda were dark.

"My has been picking pepper spunk again,"
Moominpappa said. "Last year she collected flybane."

"Let's hope she takes to chanterelles next autumn,"
said Moominmamma. "Or at least to something not
directly poisonous."

"Hope for the best and prepare for the worst," little
My observed with a chuckle.

They continued their work in peaceful silence.

Suddenly there were a few light taps on the glass pane in the door, and without waiting for an answer Too-ticky came in and shook the rain off her oilskin jacket. Then she held the door open and called out in the dark: "Well, come along!"

"Whom are you bringing?" Moomintroll asked.

"It's Ninny," Too-ticky said. "Yes, her name's Ninny."

She still held the door open, waiting. No one came.

"Oh, well," Too-ticky said and shrugged her shoulders. "If she's too shy she'd better stay there for a while."

"She'll be drenched through," said Moominmamma.

"Perhaps that won't matter much when one's invisible," Too-ticky said and sat down by the table. The family stopped working and waited for an explanation.

"You all know, don't you, that if people are frightened very often, they sometimes become invisible," Too-ticky said and swallowed a small egg mushroom that looked like a little snowball. "Well. This Ninny was frightened the wrong way by a lady who had taken care of her without really liking her. I've met this lady, and she was horrid. Not the angry sort, you know, which would have been understandable. No, she was the icily ironical kind."

"What's ironical?" Moomintroll asked.

"Well, imagine that you slip on a rotten mushroom and sit down on the basket of newly picked ones," Too-ticky said. "The natural thing for your mother would be to be angry. But no, she isn't. Instead she says, very coldly: 'I understand that's your idea of a graceful dance, but I'd thank you not to do it in people's food.' Something like that."

"How unpleasant," Moomintroll said.

"Yes, isn't it," replied Too-ticky. "This was the way this lady used to talk. She was ironic all day long every day, and finally the kid started to turn pale and fade around the edges, and less and less was seen of her. Last Friday one couldn't catch sight of her at all. The lady gave her away to me and said she really couldn't take care of relatives she couldn't see."

"And what did you do to the lady?" My asked with bulging eyes. "Did you bash her head?"

"That's of no use with the ironic sort," Too-ticky said. "I took Ninny home with me, of course. And now I've brought her here for you to make her visible again."

There was a slight pause. Only the rain was heard, rustling along over the veranda roof. Everybody stared at Too-ticky and thought for a while.

"Does she talk?" Moominpappa asked.

"No. But the lady has hung a small silver bell around her neck so that one can hear where she is."

Too-ticky arose and opened the door again. "Ninny!" she called out in the dark.

The cool smell of autumn crept in from the garden, and a square of light threw itself on the wet grass. After a while there was a slight tinkle outside, rather hesitantly. The sound came up the steps and stopped. A bit above the floor a small silver bell was seen hanging in the air on a black ribbon. Ninny seemed to have a very thin neck.

"All right," Too-ticky said. "Now, here's your new family. They're a bit silly at times, but rather decent, largely speaking."

"Give the kid a chair," Moominpappa said. "Does she know how to pick mushrooms?"

"I really know nothing at all about Ninny," Too-ticky said. "I've only brought her here and told you what I know. Now I have a few other things to attend to. Please look in some day, won't you, and let me know how you get along. Cheerio."

When Too-ticky had gone the family sat quite silent, looking at the empty chair and the silver bell. After a while one of the chanterelles slowly rose from the heap on the table. Invisible paws picked it clean from needles and earth. Then it was cut to pieces, and the pieces drifted away and laid themselves in the basin. Another mushroom sailed up from the table.

"Thrilling!" My said with awe. "Try to give her something to eat. I'd like to know if you can see the food when she swallows it."

"How on earth does one make her visible again?" Moominpappa said worriedly. "Should we take her to a doctor?"

"I don't think so," said Moominmamma. "I believe she wants to be invisible for a while. Too-ticky said she's shy. Better leave the kid alone until something turns up."

And so it was decided.

The eastern attic room happened to be unoccupied, so Moominmamma made Ninny a bed there. The silver bell tinkled along after her upstairs and reminded Moominmamma of the cat that once had lived with them. At the bedside she laid out the apple, the glass of juice, and the three striped pieces of candy everybody in the house was given at bedtime.

Then she lighted a candle and said:

"Now have a good sleep, Ninny. Sleep as late as you can. There'll be tea for you in the morning any time you want. And if you happen to get a funny feeling or if you want anything, just come downstairs and tinkle."

Moominmamma saw the quilt raise itself to form a very small mound. A dent appeared in the pillow. She went downstairs again to her own room and started looking through Granny's old notes about Infallible Household Remedies. Evil Eye. Melancholy. Colds. No. There didn't seem to be anything suitable. Yes, there was. Towards the end of the notebook she found a few lines written down at the time when Granny's hand was already rather shaky. "If people start getting misty and difficult to see." Good. Moominmamma read the recipe, which was rather complicated, and started at once to mix the medicine for little Ninny.

The bell came tinkling downstairs, one step at a time, with a small pause between each step. Moomintroll had waited for it all morning. But the silver bell wasn't the exciting thing. That was the paws. Ninny's paws were coming down the steps. They were very small, with anxiously bunched toes. Nothing else of Ninny was visible. It was very odd.

Moomintroll drew back behind the porcelain stove and stared bewitchedly at the paws that passed him on their way to the veranda. Now she served herself some tea. The cup was raised in the air and sank back again. She ate some bread and butter and marmalade. Then the cup and saucer drifted away to the kitchen, were washed and put away in the closet. You see, Ninny was a very orderly little child.

Moomintroll rushed out in the garden and shouted: "Mamma! She's got paws! You can see her paws!"

I thought as much, Moominmamma was thinking where she sat high in the apple tree. Granny knew a thing or two. Now when the medicine starts to work we'll be on the right way.

"Splendid," said Moominpappa. "And better still when she shows her snout one day. It makes me feel sad to talk with people who are invisible. And who never answer me."

"Hush, dear," Moominmamma said warningly. Ninny's paws were standing in the grass among the fallen apples.

"Hello Ninny," shouted My. "You've slept like a hog. When are you going to show your snout? You must look a fright if you've wanted to be invisible."

"Shut up," Moomintroll whispered, "she'll be hurt." He went running up to Ninny and said:

"Never mind My. She's hardboiled. You're really safe here among us. Don't even think about that horrid lady. She can't come here and take you away. . . ."

In a moment Ninny's paws had faded away and become nearly indistinguishable from the grass.

"Darling, you're an ass," said Moominmamma. "You can't go about reminding the kid about those things. Now pick apples and don't talk rubbish."

They all picked apples.

After a while Ninny's paws became clearer again and climbed one of the trees.

It was a beautiful autumn morning. The shadows made one's snout a little chilly but the sunshine felt nearly like summer. Everything was wet from the night's rain, and all colors were strong and clear. When all the apples were picked or shaken down Moominpappa carried the biggest apple mincer out in the garden, and they started making apple-cheese.

Moomintroll turned the handle, Moominmamma fed the mincer with apples, and Moominpappa carried the filled jars to the veranda. Little My sat in a tree singing the Big Apple Song.

Suddenly there was a crash.

On the garden path appeared a large heap of apple-cheese, all prickly with glass splinters. Beside the heap one could see Ninny's paws, rapidly fading away.

"Oh," said Moominmamma. "That was the jar we use to give to the bumblebees. Now we needn't carry it down to the field. And Granny always said that if you want the earth to grow something for you, then you have to give it a present in the autumn."

167

Ninny's paws appeared back again, and above them a pair of spindly legs came to view. Above the legs one could see the faint outline of a brown dress hem.

"I can see her legs!" cried Moomintroll.

"Congrats," said little My, looking down out of her tree. "Not bad. But the Groke knows why you must wear snuff-brown."

Moominmamma nodded to herself and sent a thought to her Granny and the medicine.

Ninny padded along after them all day. They became used to the tinkle and no longer thought Ninny very remarkable.

By evening they had nearly forgotten about her. But when everybody was in bed Moominmamma took out a rose-pink shawl of hers and made it into a little dress. When it was ready she carried it upstairs to the eastern attic room and cautiously laid it out on a chair. Then she made a broad hair ribbon out of the material left over.

Moominmamma was enjoying herself tremendously. It was exactly like sewing doll's clothes again. And the funny thing was that one didn't know if the doll had yellow or black hair.

The following day Ninny had her dress on. She was visible up to her neck, and when she came down to morning tea she bobbed and piped:

"Thank you all ever so much."

The family felt very embarrassed, and no one found anything to say. Also it was hard to know where to look when one talked to Ninny. Of course one tried to look a bit above the bell where Ninny was supposed to have her eyes. But then very easily one found oneself staring at some of the visible things further down instead, and it gave one an impolite feeling.

Moominpappa cleared his throat. "We're happy to see," he started, "that we see more of Ninny today. The more we see the happier we are. . . ."

My gave a laugh and banged the table with her spoon. "Fine that you've started talking," she said. "Hope you have anything to say. Do you know any good games?"

"No," Ninny piped. "But I've heard about games."

Moomintroll was delighted. He decided to teach Ninny all the games he knew.

After coffee all three of them went down to the river to play. Only Ninny turned out to be quite impossible. She bobbed and nodded and very seriously replied, quite, and how funny, and of course, but it was clear to all that she played only from politeness and not to have fun.

"Run, run, can't you!" My cried. "Or can't you even jump?"

Ninny's thin legs dutifully ran and jumped. Then she stood still again with arms dangling. The empty dress neck over the bell was looking strangely helpless.

"D'you think anybody likes that?" My cried. "Haven't you any life in you? D'you want a biff on the nose?"

"Rather not," Ninny piped humbly.

"She can't play," mumbled Moomintroll.

"She can't get angry," little My said. "That's what's wrong with her. Listen, you," My continued and went close to Ninny with a menacing look. "You'll never have a face of your own until you've learned to fight. Believe me."

"Yes, of course," Ninny replied, cautiously backing away.

There was no further turn for the better.

At last they stopped trying to teach Ninny to play. She didn't like funny stories either. She never laughed at the right places. She never laughed at all, in fact. This had a depressing effect on the person who told the story. And she was left alone to herself.

Days went by, and Ninny was still without a face. They became accustomed to seeing her pink dress marching along behind Moominmamma. As soon as Moominmamma stopped, the silver bell also stopped, and when she continued her way the bell began tinkling again. A bit above the dress a big rose-pink bow was bobbing in thin air.

Moominmamma continued to treat Ninny with Granny's medicine, but nothing further happened. So after some time she stopped the treatment, thinking that many people had managed all right before without a head, and besides perhaps Ninny wasn't very good-looking.

Now everyone could imagine for himself what she looked like, and this can often brighten up a relationship.

One day the family went off through the wood down to the beach. They were going to pull the boat up for winter. Ninny came tinkling behind as usual, but when they came in view of the sea she suddenly stopped. Then she lay down on her stomach in the sand and started to whine.

"What's come over Ninny? Is she frightened?" asked Moominpappa.

"Perhaps she hasn't seen the sea before," Moominmamma said. She stooped and exchanged a few whispering words with Ninny. Then she straightened up again and said:

"No, it's the first time. Ninny thinks the sea's too big."

"Of all the silly kids," little My started, but Moominmamma gave her a severe look and said: "Don't be a silly kid yourself. Now let's pull the boat ashore."

They went out on the landing stage to the bathing hut where Too-ticky lived, and knocked at the door.

"Hullo," Too-ticky said, "how's the invisible child?"

"There's only her snout left," Moominpappa replied. "At the moment she's a bit startled but it'll pass over. Can you lend us a hand with the boat?"

"Certainly," Too-ticky said.

While the boat was pulled ashore and turned keel upwards Ninny had padded down to the water's edge

171

and was standing immobile on the wet sand. They left her alone.

Moominmamma sat down on the landing stage and looked down into the water. "Dear me, how cold it looks," she said. And then she yawned a bit and added that nothing exciting had happened for weeks.

Moominpappa gave Moomintroll a wink, pulled a horrible face, and started to steal up to Moominmamma from behind.

Of course he didn't really think of pushing her in the water as he had done so many times when she was young. Perhaps he didn't even want to startle her, but just to amuse the kids a little.

But before he reached her a sharp cry was heard, a pink streak of lightning shot over the landing stage, and Moominpappa let out a scream and dropped his hat into the water. Ninny had sunk her small invisible teeth in Moominpappa's tail, and they were sharp.

"Good work!" cried My. "I couldn't have done it better myself!"

Ninny was standing on the landing stage. She had a small, snub-nosed, angry face below a red tangle of hair. She was hissing at Moominpappa like a cat.

"Don't you *dare* push her into the big horrible sea!" she cried.

"I see her, I see her!" shouted Moomintroll. "She's sweet!"

"Sweet my eye," said Moominpappa, inspecting his bitten tail. "She's the silliest, nastiest, badly-brought-uppest child I've ever seen, with or without a head."

He knelt down on the landing stage and tried to fish for his hat with a stick. And in some mysterious way he managed to tip himself over, and tumbled in on his head.

He came up at once, standing safely on the bottom, with his snout above water and his ears filled with mud.

"Oh dear!" Ninny was shouting. "Oh, how great! Oh, how funny!"

The landing stage shook with her laughter.

"I believe she's never laughed before," Too-ticky said wonderingly. "You seem to have changed her, she's even worse than little My. But the main thing is that one can see her, of course."

"It's all thanks to Granny," Moominmamma said.

THE BAT-POET

Randall Jarrell

Once upon a time there was a bat—a little light brown bat, the color of coffee with cream in it. He looked like a furry mouse with wings. When I'd go in and out of my front door, in the daytime, I'd look up over my head and see him hanging upside down from the roof of the porch. He and the others hung there in a bunch, all snuggled together with their wings folded, fast asleep. Sometimes one of them would wake up for a minute and get in a more comfortable position, and then the others would wiggle around in their sleep till they'd get more comfortable too; when they all moved it looked as if a fur wave went over them. At night they'd fly up and down, around and around, and catch insects and eat them; on a rainy night, though, they'd stay snuggled together just as though it were still day. If you pointed a flashlight at them you'd see them screw up their faces to keep the light out of their eyes.

Toward the end of summer all the bats except the little brown one began sleeping in the barn. He missed them, and tried to get them to come back and sleep on the porch with him. "What do you want to sleep in the barn for?" he asked them.

"We don't know," the others said. "What do you want to sleep on the porch for?"

"It's where we always sleep," he said. "If I slept in the barn I'd be homesick. Do come back and sleep with me!" But they wouldn't.

So he had to sleep all alone. He missed the others. They had always felt so warm and furry against him; whenever he'd waked, he'd pushed himself up into the middle of them and gone right back to sleep. Now he'd wake up and, instead of snuggling against the others and going back to sleep, he would just hang there and think. Sometimes he would open his eyes a little and look out into the sunlight. It gave him a queer feeling for it to be daytime and for him to be hanging there looking; he felt the way you would feel if you woke up and went to the window and stayed there for hours, looking out into the moonlight.

It was different in the daytime. The squirrels and the chipmunk, that he had never seen before—at night they were curled up in their nests or holes, fast asleep—ate nuts and acorns and seeds, and ran after each other playing. And all the birds hopped and sang and flew;

at night they had been asleep, except for the mockingbird. The bat had always heard the mockingbird. The mockingbird would sit on the highest branch of a tree in the moonlight, and sing half the night. The bat loved to listen to him. He could imitate all the other birds—he'd even imitate the way the squirrels chattered when they were angry, like two rocks being knocked together; and he could imitate the milk bottles being put down on the porch and the barn door closing, a long, rusty squeak. And he made up songs and words all his own, that nobody else had ever said or sung.

The bat told the other bats about all the things you could see and hear in the daytime. "You'd love them," he said. "The next time you wake up in the daytime, just keep your eyes open for a while and don't go back to sleep."

The other bats were sure they wouldn't like that. "We wish we didn't wake up at all," they said. "When you wake up in the daytime the light hurts your eyes—the thing to do is to close them and go right back to sleep. Day's to sleep in; as soon as it's night we'll open our eyes."

"But won't you even try it?" the little brown bat said. "Just for once, try it."

The bats all said: "No."

"But why not?" asked the little brown bat.

The bats said: "We don't know. We just don't want to."

"At least listen to the mockingbird. When you hear him it's just like the daytime."

The other bats said: "He sounds so queer. If only he squeaked or twittered—but he keeps shouting in that bass voice of his." They said this because the mockingbird's voice sounded terribly loud and deep to them; they always made little high twittering sounds themselves.

"Once you get used to it you'll like it," the little bat said. "Once you get used to it, it sounds wonderful."

"All right," said the others, "we'll try." But they were just being polite; they didn't try.

The little brown bat kept waking up in the daytime, and kept listening to the mockingbird, until one day he thought: "*I* could make up a song like the mockingbird's." But when he tried, his high notes were all high and his low notes were all high and the notes in between were all high: he couldn't make a tune. So he imitated the mockingbird's words instead. At first his words didn't go together—even the bat could see that they didn't sound a bit like the mockingbird's. But after a while some of them began to sound beautiful, so that the bat said to himself: "If you get the words right you don't need a tune."

The bat went over and over his words till he could say them off by heart. That night he said them to the other bats. "I've made the words like the mockingbird's," he told them, "so you can tell what it's like in the daytime." Then he said to them in a deep voice—he couldn't help imitating the mockingbird—his words about the daytime:

At dawn, the sun shines like a million moons
And all the shadows are as bright as moonlight.
The birds begin to sing with all their might.
The world awakens and forgets the night.

The black-and-gray turns green-and-gold-and-blue.
The squirrels begin to—

But when he'd got this far the other bats just couldn't keep quiet any longer.

"The sun *hurts*," said one. "It hurts like getting something in your eyes."

"That's right," said another. "And shadows are black—how can a shadow be bright?"

Another one said: "What's green-and-gold-and-blue? When you say things like that we don't know what you mean."

"And it's just not real," the first one said. "When the sun rises the world goes to sleep."

"But go on," said one of the others. "We didn't mean to interrupt you."

"No, we're sorry we interrupted you," all the others said. "Say us the rest."

But when the bat tried to say them the rest he couldn't remember a word. It was hard to say anything at all, but finally he said: "I—I—tomorrow I'll say you the rest." Then he flew back to the porch. There were lots of insects flying around the light, but he didn't catch a one; instead he flew to his rafter, hung there upside down with his wings folded, and after a while went to sleep.

But he kept on making poems like the mockingbird's—only now he didn't say them to the bats. One night he saw a mother possum, with all her little white baby possums holding tight to her, eating the fallen apples under the apple tree; one night an owl swooped down on him and came so close he'd have caught him if the bat hadn't flown into a hole in the old oak by the side of the house; and another time four squirrels spent the whole morning chasing each other up and down trees, across the lawn, and over the roof. He made up poems about them all. Sometimes the poem would make him think: "It's like the mockingbird! This time it's really like the mockingbird!" But sometimes the poem would seem so bad to him that he'd get discouraged and stop in the middle, and by the next day he'd have forgotten it.

When he would wake up in the daytime and hang there looking out at the colors of the world, he would say the poems over to himself. He wanted to say them to the other bats, but then he would remember what had happened when he'd said them before. There was nobody for him to say the poems to.

One day he thought: "I could say them to the mockingbird." It got to be a regular thought of his. It was a long time, though, before he really went to the mockingbird.

The mockingbird had bad days when he would try to drive everything out of the yard, no matter what it was. He always had a peremptory, authoritative look, as if he were more alive than anything else and wanted everything else to know it; on his bad days he'd dive on everything that came into the yard—on cats and dogs, even—and strike at them with his little sharp beak and sharp claws. On his good days he didn't pay so much attention to the world, but just sang.

The day the bat went to him the mockingbird was perched on the highest branch of the big willow by the porch, singing with all his might. He was a clear gray, with white bars across his wings that flashed when he flew; every part of him had a clear, quick, decided look about it. He was standing on tiptoe, singing and singing and singing; sometimes he'd spring up into the air. This time he was singing a song about mockingbirds.

The bat fluttered to the nearest branch, hung upside down from it, and listened; finally when the mockingbird stopped just for a moment he said in his little high voice: "It's beautiful, just beautiful!"

"You like poetry?" asked the mockingbird. You could tell from the way he said it that he was surprised.

"I love it," said the bat. "I listen to you every night. Every day too. I—I—"

"It's the last poem I've composed," said the mockingbird. "It's called 'To a Mockingbird.'"

"It's wonderful," the bat said. "Wonderful! Of all the songs I ever heard you sing, it's the best."

This pleased the mockingbird—mockingbirds love to be told that their last song is the best. "I'll sing it for you again," the mockingbird offered.

"Oh, please do sing it again," said the bat. "I'd love to hear it again. Just love to! Only when you've finished could I—"

But the mockingbird had already started. He not only sang it again, he made up new parts, and sang them over and over and over; they were so beautiful that the bat forgot about his own poem and just listened. When the mockingbird had finished, the bat thought: "No, I just can't say him mine. Still, though—" He said to the mockingbird: "It's wonderful to get to hear you. I could listen to you forever."

"It's a pleasure to sing to such a responsive audience," said the mockingbird. "Anytime you'd like to hear it again just tell me."

The bat said: "Could—could—"

"Yes?" said the mockingbird.

The bat went on in a shy voice: "Do you suppose that I—that I could—"

The mockingbird said warmly: "That you could hear it again? Of course you can. I'll be delighted." And he sang it all over again. This time it was the best of all.

The bat told him so, and the mockingbird looked pleased but modest; it was easy for him to look pleased but hard for him to look modest, he was so full of himself. The bat asked him: "Do you suppose a bat could make poems like yours?"

"A *bat*?" the mockingbird said. But then he went on politely, "Well, I don't see why not. He couldn't sing them, of course—he simply doesn't have the range; but

181

that's no reason he couldn't make them up. Why, I suppose for bats a bat's poems would be ideal."

The bat said: "Sometimes when I wake up in the daytime I make up poems. Could I—I wonder whether I could say you one of *my* poems?"

A queer look came over the mockingbird's face, but he said cordially: "I'd be delighted to hear one. Go right ahead." He settled himself on his branch with a listening expression.

The bat said:

> A shadow is floating through the moonlight
> Its wings don't make a sound.
> Its claws are long, its beak is bright.
> Its eyes try all the corners of the night.
>
> It calls and calls: all the air swells and heaves
> And washes up and down like water.
> The ear that listens to the owl believes
> In death. The bat beneath the eaves,
>
> The mouse beside the stone are still as death—
> The owl's air washes them like water.
> The owl goes back and forth inside the night,
> And the night holds its breath.

When he'd finished his poem the bat waited for the mockingbird to say something; he didn't know it, but he was holding his breath.

"Why, I like it," said the mockingbird. "Technically it's quite accomplished. The way you change the rhyme-scheme's particularly effective."

The bat said: "It is?"

"Oh yes," said the mockingbird. "And it was clever of you to have that last line two feet short."

The bat said blankly: "Two feet short?"

"It's two feet short," said the mockingbird a little impatiently. "The next-to-the-last line's iambic pentameter, and the last line's iambic trimeter."

The bat looked so bewildered that the mockingbird said in a kind voice: "An iambic foot has one weak syllable and one strong syllable; the weak one comes first. That last line of yours has six syllables and the one before it has ten; when you shorten the last line like that it gets the effect of the night holding its breath."

"I didn't know that," the bat said. "I just made it like holding your breath."

"To be sure, to be sure!" said the mockingbird. "I enjoyed your poem very much. When you've made up some more do come round and say me another."

The bat said that he would, and fluttered home to his rafter. Partly he felt very good—the mockingbird had liked his poem—and partly he felt just terrible. He thought: "Why, I might as well have said it to the bats. What do I care how many feet it has? The owl nearly kills me, and he says he likes the rhyme-scheme!" He hung there upside down, thinking bitterly. After a while he said to himself: "The trouble isn't making poems, the trouble's finding somebody that will listen to them."

Before he went to sleep he said his owl poem over to himself, and it seemed to him that it was exactly like the owl. "The *owl* would like it," he thought. "If only I could say it to the owl!"

And then he thought: "That's it! I can't say it to the owl, I don't dare get that near him; but if I made up a poem about the chipmunk I could say it to the chipmunk—*he'd* be interested." The bat got so excited his fur stood up straight and he felt warm all over. He thought: "I'll go to the chipmunk and say, 'If you'll give me six crickets I'll make a poem about you.' Really I'd do it for nothing; but they don't respect something if they get it for nothing. I'll say: 'For six crickets I'll do your portrait in verse.' "

The next day, at twilight, the bat flew to the chipmunk's hole. The chipmunk had dozens of holes, but the bat had noticed that there was one he liked best and always slept in. Before long the chipmunk ran up, his cheeks bulging. "Hello," said the bat.

The instant he heard the bat the chipmunk froze; then he dived into his hole. "Wait! Wait!" the bat cried. But the chipmunk had disappeared. "Come back," the bat called. "I won't hurt you." But he had to talk for a long time before the chipmunk came back, and even then he just stuck the tip of his nose out of the hole.

The bat hardly knew how to begin, but he timidly said to the chipmunk, who listened timidly: "I thought of making this offer to—to the animals of the vicinity. You're the first one I've made it to."

The chipmunk didn't say anything. The bat gulped, and said quickly: "For only six crickets I'll do your portrait in verse."

The chipmunk said: "What are crickets?"

The bat felt discouraged. "I knew I might have to tell him about poems," he thought, "but I never thought I'd have to tell him about *crickets*." He explained: "They're little black things you see on the porch at night, by the light. They're awfully good. But that's all right about them; instead of crickets you could give me—well, this time you don't have to give me anything. It's a—an introductory offer."

The chipmunk said in a friendly voice: "I don't understand."

"I'll make you a poem about yourself," said the bat. "One just about you." He saw from the look in the chipmunk's eyes that the chipmunk didn't understand. The bat said: "I'll say you a poem about the owl, and then you'll see what it's like."

He said his poem and the chipmunk listened intently; when the poem was over the chipmunk gave a big shiver and said, "It's terrible, just terrible! Is there really something like that at night?"

The bat said: "If it weren't for that hole in the oak he'd have got *me*."

The chipmunk said in a determined voice: "I'm going to bed earlier. Sometimes when there're lots of nuts I stay out till it's pretty dark; but believe me, I'm never going to again."

The bat said: "It's a pleasure to say a poem to—to such a responsive audience. Do you want me to start on the poem about you?"

185

The chipmunk said thoughtfully: "I don't have enough holes. It'd be awfully easy to dig some more holes."

"Shall I start on the poem about you?" asked the bat.

"All right," said the chipmunk. "But could you put in lots of holes? The first thing in the morning I'm going to dig myself another."

"I'll put in a lot," the bat promised. "Is there anything else you'd like to have in it?"

The chipmunk thought for a minute and said, "Well, nuts. And seeds—those big fat seeds they have in the feeder."

"All right," said the bat. "Tomorrow afternoon I'll be back. Or day after tomorrow—I don't really know how long it will take." He and the chipmunk said goodbye to each other and he fluttered home to the porch. As soon as he got comfortably settled he started to work on the poem about the chipmunk. But somehow he kept coming back to the poem about the owl, and what the chipmunk had said, and how he'd looked. "*He* didn't say any of that two-feet-short stuff!" The bat hung there upside down, trying to work on his new poem. He was happy.

When at last he'd finished the poem—it took him longer than he'd thought—he went looking for the chipmunk. It was a bright afternoon, and the sun blazed in the bat's eyes, so that everything looked blurred and golden. When he met the chipmunk hurrying down the path that ran past the old stump, he thought: "What a beautiful color he is! Why, the fur back on his tail's rosy, almost. And those lovely black and white stripes on his back!"

"Hello," he said.

"Hello," said the chipmunk. "Is it done yet?"

"All done," said the bat happily. "I'll say it to you. It's named 'The Chipmunk's Day.' "

The chipmunk said in a pleased voice: "My day." He sat there and listened while the bat said:

> In and out the bushes, up the ivy,
> Into the hole
> By the old oak stump, the chipmunk flashes.
> Up the pole.
>
> To the feeder full of seeds he dashes,
> Stuffs his cheeks.
> The chickadee and titmouse scold him.
> Down he streaks.
>
> Red as the leaves the wind blows off the maple,
> Red as a fox,
> Striped like a skunk, the chipmunk whistles
> Past the love seat, past the mailbox,
>
> Down the path,
> Home to his warm hole stuffed with sweet
> Things to eat.
> Neat and slight and shining, his front feet
>
> Curled at his breast, he sits there while the sun
> Stripes the red west
> With its last light: the chipmunk
> Dives to his rest.

When he'd finished, the bat asked: "Do you like it?"

For a moment the chipmunk didn't say anything, then he said in a surprised, pleased voice: "Say it again." The bat said it again. When he'd finished, the chipmunk said: "Oh, it's *nice*. It all goes in and out, doesn't it?"

The bat was so pleased he didn't know what to say. "Am I really as red as that?" asked the chipmunk.

"Oh yes," the bat said.

"You put in the seeds and the hole and everything," exclaimed the chipmunk. "I didn't think you could. I thought you'd make me more like the owl." Then he said: "Say me the one about the owl."

The bat did. The chipmunk said: "It makes me shiver. Why do I like it if it makes me shiver?"

"I don't know. I see why the owl would like it, but I don't see why we like it."

"Who are you going to do now?" asked the chipmunk.

The bat said: "I don't know. I haven't thought about anybody but you. Maybe I could do a bird."

"Why don't you do the cardinal? He's red and black like me, and he eats seeds at the feeder like me—you'd be in practice."

The bat said doubtfully: "I've watched him, but I don't know him."

"I'll ask him," said the chipmunk. "I'll tell him what it's like, and then he's sure to want to."

"That's awfully nice of you," said the bat. "I'd love to do one about him. I like to watch him feed his babies."

The next day, while the bat was hanging from his rafter fast asleep, the chipmunk ran up the ivy to the porch and called to the bat: "He wants you to." The bat stirred a little and blinked his eyes, and the chipmunk said: "The cardinal wants you to. I had a hard time telling him what a poem was like, but after I did he wanted you to."

"All right," said the bat sleepily. "I'll start it tonight."

The chipmunk said: "What did you say I was as red as? I don't mean a fox. I remember that."

"As maple leaves. As leaves the wind blows off the maple."

"Oh yes, I remember now," the chipmunk said; he ran off contentedly.

When the bat woke up that night he thought, "Now I'll begin on the cardinal." He thought about how red the cardinal was, and how he sang, and what he ate, and how he fed his big brown babies. But somehow he couldn't get started.

All the next day he watched the cardinal. The bat hung from his rafter, a few feet from the feeder, and whenever the cardinal came to the feeder he'd stare at him and hope he'd get an idea. It was queer the way the cardinal cracked the sunflower seeds; instead of standing on them and hammering them open, like a titmouse, he'd turn them over and over in his beak—it gave him a thoughtful look—and all at once the seed would fall open, split in two. While the cardinal was cracking the seed his two babies stood underneath him on tiptoe, fluttering their wings and quivering all over, their mouths wide open. They were a beautiful soft bright brown—even their beaks were brown—and they were already as big as their father. Really they were old enough to feed themselves, and did whenever he wasn't there; but as long as he was there they begged and begged, till the father would fly down by one and stuff the seed in its mouth, while the other quivered and cheeped as if its heart were breaking. The father was such a beautiful clear bright red, with his tall crest the wind rippled like fur, that it didn't seem right for him to be so harried and useful and hard-working: it was like seeing a general in a red uniform washing hundreds and hundreds of dishes. The babies followed him everywhere, and kept sticking their open mouths up by his mouth—they shook all over, they begged so hard—and he never got a bite for himself.

But it was no use: no matter how much the bat watched, he never got an idea. Finally he went to the chipmunk and said in a perplexed voice: "I can't make up a poem about the cardinal."

The chipmunk said: "Why, just say what he's like, the way you did with the owl and me."

"I would if I could," the bat said, "but I can't. I don't know why I can't, but I can't. I watch him and he's just beautiful, he'd make a beautiful poem; but I can't think of anything."

"That's *queer*," the chipmunk said.

The bat said in a discouraged voice: "I guess I can't make portraits of the animals after all."

"What a shame!"

"Oh well," the bat said, "it was just so I'd have somebody to say them to. Now that I've got you I'm all right—when I get a good idea I'll make a poem about it and say it to you."

"I'll tell the cardinal you couldn't," the chipmunk said. "He won't be too disappointed, he never has heard a poem. I tried to tell him what they're like, but I don't think he really understood."

He went off to tell the cardinal, and the bat flew home. He felt relieved; it was wonderful not to have to worry about the cardinal anymore.

All morning the mockingbird had been chasing everything out of the yard—he gave you the feeling that having anything else in the world was more than he could bear. Finally he flew up to the porch, sat on the arm of the chair, and began to chirp in a loud, impatient, demanding way, until the lady who lived inside brought him out some raisins. He flew up to a branch, waited impatiently, and as soon as she was gone dived down on the raisins and ate up every one. Then he flew over the willow and began to sing with all his might.

The bat clung to his rafter, listening drowsily. Sometimes he would open his eyes a little, and the sunlight and the shadows and the red and yellow and orange branches waving in the wind made a kind of blurred pattern, so that he would blink, and let his eyelids steal together, and go contentedly back to sleep. When he woke up it was almost dark; the sunlight was gone, and the red and yellow and orange leaves were all gray, but the mockingbird was still singing.

The porch light was lit, and there were already dozens of insects circling round it. As the bat flew toward them he felt hungry but comfortable.

Just then the mockingbird began to imitate a jay—not the way a jay squawks or scolds but the way he really sings, in a deep soft voice; as he listened the bat remembered how the mockingbird had driven off two jays that morning. He thought: "It's queer the way he drives everything off and then imitates it. You wouldn't think that—"

And at that instant he had an idea for a poem. The insects were still flying round and round the light, the mockingbird was still imitating the jay, but the bat didn't eat and he didn't listen; he flapped slowly and thoughtfully back to his rafter and began to work on the poem.

When he finally finished it—he worked on it off and on for two nights—he flew off to find the chipmunk. "I've got a new one," he said happily.

"What's it about?"

"The mockingbird."

"The mockingbird!" the chipmunk repeated. "Say it to me." He was sitting up with his paws on his chest, looking intently at the bat—it was the way he always listened.

The bat said:

Look one way and the sun is going down,
Look the other and the moon is rising.
The sparrow's shadow's longer than the lawn.
The bats squeak: "Night is here," the birds cheep:
        "Day is gone."
On the willow's highest branch, monopolizing
Day and night, cheeping, squeaking, soaring,
The mockingbird is imitating life.

All day the mockingbird has owned the yard.
As light first woke the world, the sparrows trooped
Onto the seedy lawn: the mockingbird
Chased them off shrieking. Hour by hour, fighting hard
To make the world his own, he swooped
On thrushes, thrashers, jays, and chickadees—
At noon he drove away a big black cat.

Now, in the moonlight, he sits here and sings.
A thrush is singing, then a thrasher, then a jay—
Then, all at once, a cat begins meowing.
A mockingbird can sound like anything.
He imitates the world he drove away
So well that for a minute, in the moonlight,
Which one's the mockingbird? Which one's the world?

When he had finished, the chipmunk didn't say anything; the bat said uneasily, "Did you like it?"

For a minute the chipmunk didn't answer him. Then he said: "It really is like him. You know, he's chased me. And can he imitate me! You wouldn't think he'd drive you away *and* imitate you. You wouldn't think he could."

The bat could see that what the chipmunk said meant that he liked the poem, but he couldn't keep from saying: "You do like it?"

The chipmunk said, "Yes, I like it. But he won't like it."

"You liked the one about you," the bat said.

"Yes," the chipmunk answered. "But he won't like the one about him."

The bat said: "But it *is* like him."

The chipmunk said: "Just like. Why don't you go say it to him? I'll go with you."

When they found the mockingbird—it was one of his good days—the bat told him that he had made up a new poem. "Could I say it to you?" he asked. He sounded timid—guilty almost.

"To be sure, to be sure!" answered the mockingbird, and put on his listening expression.

The bat said, "It's a poem about—well, about mockingbirds."

The mockingbird repeated: "About mockingbirds!" His face had changed, so that he had to look listening all over again. Then the bat repeated to the mockingbird his poem about the mockingbird. The mockingbird listened intently, staring at the bat; the chipmunk listened intently, staring at the mockingbird.

When the bat had finished, nobody said anything. Finally the chipmunk said: "Did it take you long to make it up?"

Before the bat could answer, the mockingbird exclaimed angrily: "You sound as if there were something wrong with imitating things!"

"Oh no," the bat said.

"Well then, you sound as if there were something wrong with driving them off. It's my territory, isn't it? If you can't drive things off your own territory what can you do?"

The bat didn't know what to say; after a minute the chipmunk said uneasily, "He just meant it's odd to drive them all off and then imitate them so well too."

"Odd!" cried the mockingbird. "Odd! If I didn't it really would be odd. Did you ever hear of a mockingbird that didn't?"

The bat said politely: "No indeed. No, it's just what mockingbirds do do. That's really why I made up the poem about it—I admire mockingbirds so much, you know."

The chipmunk said: "He talks about them all the time."

"A mockingbird's *sensitive*," said the mockingbird; when he said *sensitive* his voice went way up and way back down. "They get on my nerves. You just don't understand how much they get on my nerves. Sometimes I think if I can't get rid of them I'll go crazy."

"If they didn't get on your nerves so, maybe you wouldn't be able to imitate them so well," the chipmunk said in a helpful, hopeful voice.

"And the way they sing!" cried the mockingbird. "One two three, one two three—the same thing, the same thing, always the same old thing! If only they'd just once sing something different!"

The bat said: "Yes, I can see how hard on you it must be. I meant for the poem to show that, but I'm afraid I must not have done it right."   .

"You just haven't any *idea*!" the mockingbird went on, his eyes flashing and his feathers standing up. "Nobody but a mockingbird has any *idea*!"

The bat and the chipmunk were looking at the mockingbird with the same impressed, uneasy look. From then on they were very careful what they said— mostly they just listened, while the mockingbird told them what it was like to be a mockingbird. Toward the end he seemed considerably calmer and more cheerful, and even told the bat he had enjoyed hearing his poem.

The bat looked pleased, and asked the mockingbird: "Did you like the way I rhymed the first lines of the stanzas and then didn't rhyme the last two?"

The mockingbird said shortly: "I didn't notice"; the chipmunk told the mockingbird how much he always enjoyed hearing the mockingbird sing; and, a little later, the bat and the chipmunk told the mockingbird goodbye.

When they had left, the two of them looked at each other and the bat said: "You were right."

"Yes," said the chipmunk. Then he said: "I'm glad I'm not a mockingbird."

"I'd like to be because of the poems," the bat said, "but as long as I'm not, I'm glad I'm not."

"He thinks that he's different from everything else," the chipmunk said, "and he is."

The bat said, just as if he hadn't heard the chipmunk: "I wish I could make up a poem about bats."

The chipmunk asked: "Why don't you?"

"If I had one about bats maybe I could say it to the bats."

"That's right."

For weeks he wished that he had the poem. He would hunt all night, and catch and eat hundreds and hundreds of gnats and moths and crickets, and all the time he would be thinking: "If only I could make up a poem about bats!" One day he dreamed that it was done and that he was saying it to them, but when he woke up all he could remember was the way it ended:

> At sunrise, suddenly the porch was bats:
> A thousand bats were hanging from the rafter.

It had sounded wonderful in his dream, but now it just made him wish that the bats still slept on the porch. He felt cold and lonely. Two squirrels had climbed up in the feeder and were making the same queer noise—a kind of whistling growl—to scare each other away; somewhere on the other side of the house the mockingbird was singing. The bat shut his eyes.

For some reason, he began to think of the first things he could remember. Till a bat is two weeks old he's never alone: the little naked thing—he hasn't even any fur—clings to his mother wherever she goes. After that she leaves him at night; and the other babies hang there sleeping, till at last their mothers come home to them. Sleepily, almost dreaming, the bat began to make up a poem about a mother and her baby.

It was easier than the other poems, somehow: all he had to do was remember what it had been like and every once in a while put in a rhyme. But easy as it was, he kept getting tired and going to sleep, and would forget parts and have to make them over. When at last he finished he went to say it to the chipmunk.

The trees were all bare, and the wind blew the leaves past the chipmunk's hole; it was cold. When the chipmunk stuck his head out it looked fatter than the bat had ever seen it. The chipmunk said in a slow, dazed voice: "It's all full. My hole's all full." Then he exclaimed surprisedly to the bat: "How fat you are!"

"I?" the bat asked. "I'm fat?" Then he realized it was so; for weeks he had been eating and eating and eating. He said: "I've done my poem about the bats. It's about a mother and her baby."

"Say it to me."

The bat said:

> A bat is born
> Naked and blind and pale.
> His mother makes a pocket of her tail
> And catches him. He clings to her long fur

By his thumbs and toes and teeth.
And then the mother dances through the night
Doubling and looping, soaring, somersaulting—
Her baby hangs on underneath.
All night, in happiness, she hunts and flies.
Her high sharp cries
Like shining needlepoints of sound
Go out into the night and, echoing back,
Tell her what they have touched.
She hears how far it is, how big it is,
Which way it's going:
She lives by hearing.
The mother eats the moths and gnats she catches
In full flight; in full flight
The mother drinks the water of the pond
She skims across. Her baby hangs on tight.
Her baby drinks the milk she makes him
In moonlight or starlight, in mid-air.
Their single shadow, printed on the moon
Or fluttering across the stars,
Whirls on all night; at daybreak
The tired mother flaps home to her rafter.
The others all are there.
They hang themselves up by their toes,
They wrap themselves in their brown wings.
Bunches upside down, they sleep in air.
Their sharp ears, their sharp teeth, their quick
    sharp faces
Are dull and slow and mild.
All the bright day, as the mother sleeps,
She folds her wings about her sleeping child.

When the bat had finished, the chipmunk said: "It's all really so?"

"Why, of course," the bat said.

"And you do all that too? If you shut your eyes and make a noise you can hear where I am and which way I'm going?"

"Of course."

The chipmunk shook his head and said wonderingly: "You bats sleep all day and fly all night, and see with your ears, and sleep upside down, and eat while you're flying and drink while you're flying, and turn somersaults in mid-air with your baby hanging on, and—and—it's really queer."

The bat said: "Did you like the poem?"

"Oh, of course. Except I forgot it was a poem. I just kept thinking how queer it must be to be a bat."

The bat said: "No, it's not queer. It's wonderful to fly all night. And when you sleep all day with the others it feels wonderful."

The chipmunk yawned. "The end of it made me all sleepy," he said. "But I was already sleepy. I'm sleepy all the time now."

The bat thought, "Why, I am too." He said to the chipmunk: "Yes, it's winter. It's almost winter."

"You ought to say the poem to the other bats," the chipmunk said. "They'll like it just the way I liked the one about me."

"Really?"

"I'm sure of it. When it has all the things you do, you can't help liking it."

"Thank you so much for letting me say it to you," the bat said. "I *will* say it to them. I'll go say it to them now."

"Goodbye," said the chipmunk. "I'll see you soon. Just as soon as I wake up I'll see you."

"Goodbye," the bat said.

The chipmunk went back into his hole. It was strange to have him move so heavily, and to see his quick face so slow. The bat flew slowly off to the barn. In the west, over the gray hills, the sun was red: in a little while the bats would wake up and he could say them the poem.

High up under the roof, in the farthest corner of the barn, the bats were hanging upside down, wrapped in their brown wings. Except for one, they were fast asleep. The one the little brown bat lighted by was asleep; when he felt someone light by him he yawned, and screwed his face up, and snuggled closer to the others. "As soon as he wakes up I'll say it to him," the bat thought. "No, I'll wait till they're all awake." On the other side of him was the bat who was awake: that one gave a big yawn, snuggled closer to the others, and went back to sleep.

The bat said to himself sleepily: "I wish I'd said we sleep all winter. That would have been a good thing to have in." He yawned. He thought: "It's almost dark.

201

As soon as it's dark they'll wake up and I'll say them the poem. The chipmunk said they'd love it." He began to say the poem over to himself; he said in a soft contented whisper,

> A bat is born
> Naked and blind and pale.
> His mother makes a pocket of her tail
> And catches him. He clings—he clings—

He tried to think of what came next, but he couldn't remember. It was about fur, but he couldn't remember the words that went with it. He went back to the beginning. He said,

> A bat is born
> Naked and blind—

but before he could get any further he thought: "I wish I'd said we sleep all winter." His eyes were closed; he yawned, and screwed his face up, and snuggled closer to the others.

ACKNOWLEDGMENTS

All possible care has been taken to trace ownership and secure permission for each selection in this series. The Great Books Foundation wishes to thank the following authors, publishers, and representatives for permission to reprint copyrighted material:

Charles, from THE LOTTERY, by Shirley Jackson. Copyright 1948, 1949 by Shirley Jackson; renewed 1976, 1977 by Laurence Hyman, Barry Hyman, Mrs. Sarah Webster, and Mrs. Joanne Schnurer. Reprinted by permission of Farrar, Straus and Giroux, Inc.

Ghost Cat, from EERIE ANIMALS: SEVEN STORIES, by Donna Hill. Copyright 1983 by Donna Hill. Reprinted by permission of the author.

Turquoise Horse, from TURTLE DREAM: COLLECTED STORIES FROM THE HOPI, NAVAJO, PUEBLO, AND HAVASUPAI PEOPLE, by Gerald Hausman. Copyright 1989 by Gerald Hausman. Published by Mariposa Publishing. Reprinted by permission of the author.

MAURICE'S ROOM, by Paula Fox. Copyright 1966 by Paula Fox. Reprinted by permission of Macmillan Publishing Company.

Barbie, from BASEBALL IN APRIL AND OTHER STORIES, by Gary Soto. Copyright 1990 by Gary Soto. Reprinted by permission of Harcourt Brace Jovanovich, Inc.

Lenny's Red-Letter Day, from I'M TRYING TO TELL YOU, by Bernard Ashley. Copyright 1981 by Bernard Ashley. First published in 1981 by Kestrel Books. Reprinted by permission of Penguin Books Limited.

TRAMP, by Malcolm Carrick. Copyright 1977 by Malcolm Carrick. Reprinted by permission of HarperCollins Publishers.

Alberic the Wise, from ALBERIC THE WISE AND OTHER JOURNEYS, by Norton Juster. Copyright 1965 by Norton Juster. Reprinted by permission of Sterling Lord Literistic, Inc.

Podhu and Aruwa, from TALES TOLD NEAR A CROCODILE, by Humphrey Harman. Copyright 1962 by Humphrey Harman. Reprinted by permission of Century Hutchinson Publishing Group Limited.

The Invisible Child, from TALES FROM MOOMINVALLEY, by Tove Jansson. Translation copyright 1963 by Ernest Benn Limited. Reprinted by permission of A & C Black (Publishers) Limited.

THE BAT-POET, by Randall Jarrell. Copyright 1963, 1964 by Macmillan Publishing Company. Reprinted by permission of Macmillan Publishing Company.

ILLUSTRATION CREDITS